Strange People, Strange Country

"Come all you poor, ignorant, and oppressed"

We will assist you in our strange way

I am neither a politician nor a diplomat and so I`m not polite –
I say what I think and what I think about is what I see with my own eyes.
My job is simply to look around and to write what I see.

Anna Politkovskaya – October 2006 Moscow.

This courageous journalist of Novaya Gazeta, fearless and devoted, was murdered for her observations. Crime and inequity will persist unabated everywhere, if people do not have the courage demonstrated by Anna Politkovskaya to protect and change corrupt ways. And that certainly applies to us in the USA.

We descend from differing backgrounds and beliefs, and our thoughts concerning the conduct of our fellow citizens, social issues, economic equity, and foreign policy cover a wide range of opinions and beliefs.

Regardless we must understand the terrible harm caused through defective inequitable federal government programs and policies that only benefit dishonest politicians and undeserving vested interests at the expense of the oblivious and permissive taxpayer – you and I.

You will learn the enormous economic cost of this undemocratic distribution of the nation's wealth as it applies to you and your family, and how you and I can resolve a major problem that is destroying our quality of life. You and I have permitted Washington politicians to take advantage of us. Now is the time to recover control of our wealth for the good of all.

Paul Bulkley

Introduction

Two million homeless, ten to fifteen million unemployed, forty five to fifty million on food stamps, the majority of the nation's work force poorly paid lacking work security. Education and Health extremely expensive with low world standards. The nation's wealth held by ½% of the population – the masses have nothing! A foreign policy based on aggression throughout the planet. A nation subject to surveillance features of the worst police state.

Every educated reader no doubt is aware of these facts. What is new!

The nation's government is claimed by Washington to be democratic serving the needs of the people; that government conducts its obligations in a honest and responsible manner; a government that conducts its foreign policy with dialogue free of aggression; a government that retains and defends the highest level of standards.

However the knowledgeable reader would question such claims. He is aware of the corruption that exists in Washington through dishonest politicians, vested interests, lobbyists, and a failed federal government. What he may not aware is the extent of the corruption that has seriously affected his wallet and quality of life, has destroyed the country's economy, and bankrupted the nation.

Aristotle in his consideration of Ethics as it applied to legislators is concerned not only to the letter of the law but also the citizen's moral character. "For legislators make the citizens good by forming habits in them, and this is the wish of every legislator, and those who do not effect it miss their mark, and it is in this that a good constitution differs from a bad one". It is significant that Aristotle emphasized the crucial role of politics in the good life, not only of the community at large, but of every citizen as well. **Words alone are insufficient in order to make people good.**

It is thus of extreme concern when a nation's government does not meet desirable standards. **Of greater concern is that the nation's people remain MUTE.** There are no protests, no visible reaction, a population that appears brainwashed incapable of any form of action; an electorate that persists to imagine that Washington democratically represents their interests in all matters.

Geoffrey Lancaster rubbed his eyes. **Why did no one complain.** Why was no one concerned that 40% to 45% of the federal government annual tax outlays ($4 Trillion) was criminally diverted to dishonest vested interests and their lobbyists, through corrupt politicians and their destructive social, economic, and foreign policies, programs, and subsidies. Washington politicians were openly ignoring their first duty the concern of the nation's people.

Two men are concerned about the terrible danger faced by the nation and its people. Geoffrey Lancaster retired engineer and Richard Homes newspaper reporter meet and agree that it would appear that the economic crisis is due to corrupt politicians, lobbyists, vested interests, and irresponsible federal government personnel. Also significantly every citizen was just as guilty in permitting this criminal nonsense in Washington.

Richard Homes makes an extensive investigation interviewing individuals of all social levels recording their thoughts and reactions pertinent to a variety of unsatisfactory policies, programs, and subsidies. Were they unsatisfactory or imagined. If unsatisfactory why did no one complain. **Why was everyone silent.** Admittedly there was some evidence of unhappiness – desperate individuals, their food stamp entitlement in jeopardy, protested the irresponsible subsidies given to state farmers in Alabama. But what of the rest of the Nation?

Finally Geoffrey and Richard share findings and notes. A significant conclusion. No conventional modification to the political structure and change in Washington's behavior would provide a satisfactory solution.

Geoffrey Lancaster prepares his report and conclusion. It would be impossible to reform the conduct of the corrupt politicians. However the retired engineer devised a solution which was radical and no doubt would astound the Founding Fathers. It certainly would assist in resolving the failing nature and character of the human race, would make all better educated and responsible citizens, eliminate the current corruption in Washington, and would be beneficial to the individual, his family, nation, and the world.

Contents

A STRANGE PUZZLE

A NEWSPAPER REPORTER INTERVIEWS FELLOW CITIZENS

Country of Scams
A pile of apples
The Root of the Problem

Farmer Giles saves the World
Waste Not, Want Not
Coffee Mugs take on the Future

The Rebel 51st State
Climate Change – not Us
Education – still waiting for real change

Health Industry – Penny Wise, Shilling Foolish
Pork Barrels full of Pork
The Police State

Moving the American Way
Money down the Drain
British always so British

RICHARD´S FINDINGS SUMMARISED

GEOFFREY LANCASTER´S SOLUTION

They believe what they wish to believe.

Wise Owl sighed and asked.

"Why unhappy Man are your beliefs so often based on ignorance, greed and prejudice, when contentment is found in Understanding, Equity, and Compassion!"

A Strange Puzzle

Geoffrey Lancaster had been puzzled for many years. *What precisely makes the USA tick?*

It seemed to be a profound puzzle beyond his understanding. With a professional background in quantity surveying and construction cost planning in England, Northern Rhodesia, South Africa, Southwest Africa, and Canada, his work had always demanded his full attention. There was rarely any spare time to be a student of the nation´s history and social behavior and to understand the nature and character of the people responsible. Father´s advice that the greatest value in life was to succeed and be respected in one´s chosen profession remained firmly in his mind as the years passed by.

It was a puzzle that Geoffrey suspected explained his failure to succeed in his business that specialized in design economic planning. Now forcibly retired, there being no demand for his services, he had plenty of time to ponder over a question that seemed to demand an answer.

What precisely made the USA tick?

Subsequent to his arrival in California during the late 1960s, he became increasingly aware that wealth and power was the dominating theme of life in America. It applied to all regardless whether the individual was the president of an enormous commercial, industrial, or institutional entity, or the lowest worker seen in the street.

Wealth and power was achieved through *"Whom you know"* rather than *"What you know."*

It was significant to understand that this shared opinion of the common individual had existed for many centuries. De Tocqueville, during the early years, made the disturbing observation.

"I know of no country in which there is so little independence of mind and real freedom of discussion in America!"

In England the monk Matthew Paris, famous for his diaries written during the 1200s, commented that the French considered the Englishman a barbarian, ignorant and uneducated, a drunkard, too ready to argue, fight, and kill. Eight hundred years later the observer outside typical English pubs in villages, towns, and cities on Friday and Saturday nights might conclude that little has changed.

"Little independence of mind and real freedom of discussion!"

It may seem strange that this sad condition applied to most individuals in Great Britain, and even worse in the U.S. where the right to make decisions by the aristocracy was replaced by the common man. Democracy, one would imagine, offered the unfettered opportunity for all to think and speak. **Yet the masses are mute!** Surely there must be other factors responsible for this unfortunate and curious lack of spirit.

They believe what they wish to believe.

Wise Owl sighed and asked.

"Why unhappy Man are your beliefs so often based on ignorance, greed and prejudice, when contentment is found in Understanding, Equity, and Compassion!"

Examination of the history of the British Empire 1600 to 1950 reveals considerable activity invading and controlling foreign lands with the praiseworthy claim of improving the lives of the defeated through education and religion but clearly overshadowed by commercial development and profit which was rarely if ever enjoyed by the local people. Despite all that commercial activity and immediate profit, the cost and necessity to protect and retain the British Empire possessions basically bankrupt Great Britain, and finally it relinquished all interest.

What is of remarkable and curious is that the inhabitants of the U.S., many of whom were descendants of emigrants fleeing the lack of economic opportunity in Great Britain, created their own world empire 1700 to 2000 for commercial profit with minimal pretence of bettering the lives of foreigners and their countries. Again wealth and power has been the dominant feature, a policy created by greed, and the U.S. is now basically bankrupt having created numerous enemies throughout the world.

This observation of the past and present, although disturbing, is not the primary subject. What is of concern is how the leading echelons of U.S. society have used their wealth and power to control the country's claimed democratic political system, the development of policies and programs hostile to the interest and welfare of the individual, and the criminal distribution of the nation's taxable wealth. The nation could be the envy and leader of the world, **and yet is bankrupt with national debt liabilities approaching $17 Trillion!** It is extremely pertinent to understand that the Federal Government has not been able to repay any part of this enormous liability for many years, and has struggled with merely paying the interest on that liability!

No doubt many shrug their shoulders pretending that the problem has nothing to do with them. One should think again. Assuming there are about 150 million taxpayers, **each taxpayer and his family is liable now for about $115,000.** No problem- the national debt of $17 Trillion can be paid off immediately with every taxpayer paying their contribution. Glumly you admit that you owe enormous sums to credit card companies and banks and unable to pay this tax obligation! The question then arises. **When will you pay —next week?**

Of course it is thought provoking that the claimed leader of the Western World has **12 to 14 million** unemployed, **47 million** on food stamps, and any night throughout the nation **about 2 million** are homeless. What is incredible and extremely disturbing is the passive allowance of the electorate to permit and suffer this absurd economic and criminal inequity.

Study of Federal Government annual outlays of tax revenues - **$4 Trillion ($4,000,000,000,000)** - is extremely revealing. Possibly 45% of that enormous outlay has been diverted and awarded to criminal vested interests. Further investigation reveals that the crime is not merely the inequitable theft of the nation's wealth. **What is worse are the many policies and programs that also are very beneficial to these criminal vested interests** and are the reason for the destruction of the world's climate, the poisoning of land, water, and air, constant wars, and the ruin of foreign country economies and lives.

Most unforgivable is the nation's dominant foreign policy that is consistently aggressive rather than one of civilized dialogue, understanding, and compassion. It is a foreign policy designed for wealth and power, for the economic benefit of vested interests, and definitely not for the economic benefit of the man in the street. Foreign policy is presented as U.S.'s destiny to promote global freedom, capitalism, and democracy but in fact conceals deliberate aggression for wealth and power. There is rarely any consistency in foreign policy other than the practice of supporting foreign entities that appears to be advantageous for further gain in wealth and power. Thus so often the claimed enemy becomes the claimed friend and vise versa. There is no rational explanation. Any explanation, if demanded and available is fabricated lacking common sense, and any further dialogue is conveniently swept under the carpet.

Earnings of U.S. corporations through foreign operations contributed during the 1970s was 20% to 25% of total corporate profits after taxes. Clearly corporations have considerable influence in setting foreign policy. It has resulted in the loss of 8 million U.S. jobs and the demise of the nation's future. And yet there is no public protest. One would imagine that in a truly democratic institution, the people would protest. **But the people remain mute.**

One might excuse the ordinary man in the street through lack of education deluded with the common desire for wealth and power however remote the *"American Dream"* might be. But would not the intelligent professionals throughout the country benefitting from superior education and logic identify the faults of the current *democratic decision making system* which can only destroy the nation. The answer is negative. The subject is avoided. The very people capable of identifying a faulty and undemocratic methodology of government policy making remain basically mute. **Like their poorer cousin in the street, the intelligent professional permits the common desire for wealth and power dominate all thinking.** Criticism of government policy making is trumped by greed –the fear of losing potential business and for some the loss of one's business. It is considered not wise to *"Rock the boat"* in a country that permits police state activities, and is dominated by commercial interests.

Perhaps the ordinary man can be forgiven for taking little interest in the nation's foreign policy – his economic concerns and woes apply primarily to current local issues. Yet again there no visible concern. He does not appear to be aware that his enjoyment of the economic quality of his life is subject to *"Planned Obsolescence"* the planned destructive policies of the nation's manufacturers. The man in the street is encouraged to support a *"Throw Away Spirit"* attitude. *"Planned Quality Obsolescence"* encourages the owner to reject product desirability although the item may function well. **The nation's wealth is thrown away with irresponsible abandon.**

The intent of the manufacturers is quite obvious – **Profit and Greed**. Products with shorter and shorter life spans result in increased production and consumption. The automobile which should have a life of 40 to 50 years is often rejected within 10 to15 years. Clothing garments that should have a life of 20 to 30 years are destined inappropriate within a very short span, being described as old fashioned and not modern. Style can destroy its desirability although it's utility remains unimpaired.

It is frightening that the U.S.A with a population of about 6% of world population consumes more than 50% of the world's annual consumption of raw materials, and the cause of world environmental disasters.

The Nation's industries, although the main cause of public protest, often astutely divert public attention through creating economic fears, the loss of work, and deviously support programs attacking minor and fabricated scapegoats. Thus the coal industry and the power energy generating plants consistently complain of **increased costs, loss of jobs, and other irrelevant matters, and purposely ignore the terrible harm caused by their pollution and waste.**

The success and quality of life is dependent on the enthusiasm and confidence of the nation's people. Regardless of the skills and dominance of major industrial, commercial, and financial institutions responsible for product manufacture, intelligent technology, and banking, no nation including the USA can succeed without a satisfied and confident work force.

The harm caused by Washington's conspiracy led by presidents Bush and Clinton and the US business world with the introduction and implementation of **"Free Trade"** has been enormous. Include also the fabricated wars in the Middle East and the considerable watering down of the Dodd-Frank legislation, and the end result has been a major economic disaster.

It has been the cause of an extremely serious recession. Certainly there was a considerable economic benefit realized by all industries and commercial entities that closed down their basic operations in the U.S. and opened up in foreign countries taking advantage of cheap labor resources. Certainly vested interests, particularly weapon industries, their lobbyists, and Washington politicians all benefitted through favorable policies, programs, and omissions. **And certainly every individual in the U.S. has suffered economically with a severe lowering of their quality of life.**

Washington politicians conspiring with large American business has been the cause of this serious recession resulting in enormous profit for business and a total disaster for the ordinary individual in the street. It is a recession and disaster that has existed for many years, and the needed recovery has not been addressed meaningfully other than hypocritical and meaningless statements by Washington.

There are two million homeless, ten to fifteen million unemployed, forty five to fifty million on food stamps, and the majority of the nation's workforce poorly paid lacking work security. The nation's moral is at a very low level.

And why should the nation's moral not be at a low level. Consider the disgraceful and deplorable action and inaction of Washington to solve their self created economic disaster and recession. Economic solutions that are at the expence of the man in the street. Shut down unemployment entitlements; Reduce Food Stamp entitlements; Introduce a National Health scheme that permits the Health Industry to continue its criminal costs and low standards, and does not address the real health and economic needs of the poor.

Yes. You may sniff. You imagine that these so called problems are the concern of others. You are so wrong. This recession is an economic disaster that affects everyone. Your bank account may appear untouched but your standard and quality of living is going down, down, and down.

The country is becoming increasingly shabby. Whether one views the commercial or residential world, all is becoming more and more shabby. Examine the untidy cheap sloppy clothing of all, the general unhappiness and fortitude in the streets, the crowds that visit the $1 Stores and Goodwill, the sad tales heard on the radio of individuals in despair having searched for years for employment.

For those that scorn, go to Europe and review carefully the standard of living of the average individual. Even in England which is a poor example of wise economic planning, it is common to learn that everyone has their annual holiday abroad, travel on cruise ships, national health, and the best in their residence. Examine in Europe the wonderful public structures, transportation systems, health and education services, and the general dynamic sense in the streets. Where does that exist in the U.S.?

Finally, because all of you are dominated by evaluating anything by "Cost" regardless of utility and social values, consider the true cost of this economic recession. (1) This financial crisis has diminished the standard and quality of living. (2) 45 to 50 million are on food stamps, 2 million are homeless, and 8 to 15 million unemployed. (3) The American workforce, as it exists, is underpaid and lack work security.

It is imperative to realize that all these millions of people need economic assistance. In addition the State suffers through the fact that none of these individuals are contributing to the nation´s taxation system, and the nation´s economy and moral suffers accordingly.

How much is this recession costing you?

- The National Debt per taxpayer $18 Trillion
- Supporting the unemployed and sick $150 Billion   -year
- Loss of taxable incomes   - unemployed $30   Billion   -year
- Loss of taxable incomes   - poorly paid $90   Billion   -year
- Destruction of public facilities – lack of maintenance $xxx Trillion   -huge
- Remedial work resolving environmental damage $xxx Trillion   -huge

A debt obligation of $25 Trillion represents a cost to each individual taxpayer (assumed to be 150 million) of $166,000. Payment by Bit Coin not acceptable!

Well that is more than enough complaining. More important and valuable is to devise a solution. The current system is guaranteed to destroy the nation and its people through greed and its unwillingness to consider others. There will be no winners whether their purpose is a desire for wealth and power or not. The solution will have to identify and recognize the failing nature of the human race, and design a policy and programs that will avoid or control these faults. The policy and programs will be established with common sense, intelligence, and an enforced obligation of all to work for a common cause.

But what is the solution and how will it be implemented?

Geoffrey Lancaster rubbed eyes tired in despair. The day´s editorial reported that **over $500 million ($0.5 Billion) was spent annually** by the Health Industry lobbyists in Washington seeking favorable policies and programs for their clients. No wonder the criminal Health Industry in the USA is the most expensive in the world, double the cost of European systems, and significantly very much inferior. He was well aware that the Health Industry was merely one of many vested interests. One had to realize that every conceivable business had lobbyists busy beating the doors of Washington with their graft and bribes demanding favorable terms and contacts. No wonder all political representatives in Washington are millionaires. Something has to be done to end this criminal state of affairs.

Health Industry was only one of many vested interests. One has to understand that every conceivable business had lobbyists busy beating the doors of Washington with their graft and bribes demanding favorable terms and contacts. No wonder all political representatives in Washington are millionaires. Something has to be done to end this criminal state of affairs.

Geoffrey spoke to Richard Homes news reporter for the local newspaper, and asked his advice and assistance. He seemed the ideal individual consistently in communication with people.

"Have you any ideas how this problem can be identified and resolved?"

Richard smiled sadly. There had to be better candidates than he for Geoffrey's complex and demanding puzzle. Reluctantly he accepted that he was trapped. Geoffrey had provided a great service for him resolving a serious construction contract dispute some years past. Richard was now the ideal individual, and he would return with suggestions how the problem might be addressed. Later that week he gave the puzzle further thought, and gradually became enthused.

"What truly made America tick?"

Richard returned a few weeks later after giving Geoffrey's puzzle some consideration. He did not have any specific convictions but was confident that interviewing local people regarding a variety of social and economic problems would eventually reveal a common factor. With some confidence he explained.

"With due respect to your concern, I think a list of topics should be addressed which identify perceived problems, and record the thinking and reaction of the typical guy in the street."

Geoffrey nodded. Richard's proposal was sound. It made sense to record the thoughts and response of those interviewed. The retired professional cautiously warned that the exercises would be improved if Richard did not give the interviewed any assistance. He asked the reporter.

"Have you a list of topics?"

Richard in a very business fashion pulled out a sheet of paper with the list of topics set out.

"Difficulty is keeping the list short. Anyhow this list seems adequate"

He slid the list across the table for Geoffrey's examination. The list was quite detailed, but what was of particular interest was his explanation of his choice of topics.

"I think many of the topics are pretty obvious but I will give you my 5 cents worth."

Richard leaned back, stared at his list, and talked for over two hours! Briefly his concerns addressed the following:

The Farming Industry: The subsidies given to the Farming Industry is an absolute disgrace. Nearly 50 million people in this country are on Food Stamps, 10 to 15 million unemployed, and 2 million any night without a roof over their heads. And yet enormous subsidies are given to farmers in order to not grow crops, to grow crops that can be purchased cheaper elsewhere, and to grow huge crops of corn for Ethanol whilst the fuel can be purchased cheaper from Brazil. And these farmers are wealthy!

Illegal Emigrants and Poverty Level Wages: The nation permits an enormous number of illegal emigrants to work in this country at wages well below poverty level. These illegal emigrants are holding jobs which should be held by the large number of unemployed citizens. Companies and individuals are permitted to operate scams taking advantage of naïve and desperate individuals seeking work. Too often the scam offers little or no meaningful remuneration. Finally permitting this illegal emigration encourages these individuals not to respect laws, is the cause of additional crime, and a major tax burden supporting possibly four million illegal families who should not be in the country.

 A Nation in which there is little independence of mind and real freedom of discussion: So much of the population comprise of people incapable of independent thought. Observe the absurd habits adopted by individuals who copy each other like sheep. Industry and Commerce speak enthusiastically of their products being green. Well quite possibly the greenest product in the U.S. is not manufactured. It is the dense greenness located between the ears of its citizens.

The Education Disaster: This disaster is due the lack of meaningful standards in education and the mandatory need to recognize that we are all different. Our interests and our ability to learn differ considerably. It is not a reflection of our intelligence. Enormous sums are invested in educational facilities that are not planned and designed economically and represent considerable functional and economic waste.

Population Control: *This subject is as important as Climate Change, and yet everyone is afraid to even discuss birth control and the necessity to limit families to one child. Just as frightening is the evidence of the world's inability, individual country's inability, and this nation's inability to support current populations. And yet the U.S. continues to permit millions of emigrants to enter the country.*

Public denial - the cause of Climate Change: *The U.S. population is 6% of the world population and yet consumes over 50% of the world's materials. Over the past fifty years, people have been increasingly warned of their wasteful habits and the impending environmental harm to both the nation and world. And yet inaction and denial persists, and increasingly environmental disasters of considerable magnitude occur. It is a country of selfish individuals incapable of thinking and taking logical action.*

Criminal Foreign Policy: *A policies and programs that have caused the death of 20 to 25 million throughout the planet over the past one hundred years; policies and programs that only favors vested U.S commercial interests desiring wealth and power.*

The Health Industry: *– the shame of the world. It is planned and designed to cater for the rich, and is incredibly costly. There is no meaningful medical and health care for the poor. Despite the cost of the current system, the Industry standards compare very badly with other nations that have nationalized health care.*

Distribution of the nation's annual taxable wealth: *$4,000,000,000,000 **($4 Trillion)** is distributed to Federal Government Departments. Through Federal Government mismanagement and Washington corruption, at least **$1.5 Trillion to $2 Trillion** is wasted with no benefit to the taxpayers. Much of this wasted money ends up in the pockets of vested interests. Corruption in Washington must end otherwise this country and its citizens will be economically and physically destroyed.*

Pork Barrel Projects: *Considerable funds are constantly allocated for Federal projects dreamt up to favor a specific politician's constituency. Often the projects have questionable utility and certainly they are not in the interest and benefit of the nation.*

Law Enforcement out of Control: *We like to think we live in the information age, when daily or even second by second statistics on such fare as stock prices and the annual number of homicides are at our fingertips. For all the careful accounting, however, there are two figures Americans don't have: the precise number of people killed by the police, and the number of times police use excessive force. There is no comprehensive accounting of the nation's 17,000 police departments. **And worse any review of***

irresponsible and illegal activities by the police is commonly made by their peers – the police are never at fault!

Inefficient Transportation Systems: *There are currently eight million (8,000,000) heavy and medium trucks operating on the nation's highways. On major highways the ratio of trucks to automobiles is between one in two and one in three! The enormous environmental damage caused by this form of transportation must be eliminated by moving all freight by rail. The private use of the automobile is destroying the utility of cities, is inefficient and unnecessary, and must be replaced by public transportation and appropriate restrictions.*

Uneconomic Construction: *Approximately **$1 Trillion** is spent annually on Construction – roughly 65% private and 35% public. Meaningful unbiased and skilled design economic planning is extremely rare. Between $50 billion and $100 billion can be saved through correct design economic decisions made at the right time.*

Public Waste in Social Behavior: *Whether or not one is concerned about the plight of the homeless **(643,000)** and those seeking shelter **(1.56 million)**, a fortune can be saved by resolving the problem. Another example of considerable waste is the deplorable and unnecessary habits of the nation's individual driver. It is the cause of intolerable and ridiculous traffic conditions and serious environmental pollution.*

The Drug Problem: *It is a problem because Washington has deemed it a crime! A crime just as ridiculous when Washington deemed alcohol consumption in the 1930s to be a crime. Vested interests benefit from these absurd restrictive laws, and are responsible for their continuance. The U.S. is one of the only countries in the world that persists in this ridiculous state of affairs that has doubled or more the prison population. The cost to society is enormous with about 7.5 million individuals either incarcerated or on probation!*

Excessive Waste: *Excessive waste can be identified everywhere. Poorly designed buildings result in excessive heat transfer. Irresponsible planning and use of water results in excessive water consumption. Unnecessary Commercial and Retail packaging designed for appearance rather than for utility. Single use plastic bags for shopping are a national garbage disaster. The disposal of unwanted vehicles, boats, appliances, and industrial waste a major cause of litter. The irresponsible ownership and abandonment of real estate is criminal, a health hazard, and a national disgrace.*

Richard ran long fingers through his hair. Although he had completed his list in a thorough manner, he was aware that there were many other matters that could be considered, and concluded.

"I could present many more topics but that list is more than sufficient."

Geoffrey nodded enthusiastically. Richard's list was more than ample, and adequately represented the many problems that affected directly and indirectly every man in the street. The individual's thoughts and reaction would be extremely interesting to record. Hopefully with that information a solution would be found.

A NEWSPAPER REPORTER INTERVIEWS FELLOW CITIZENS.

Richard Homes, very much occupied, postponed tackling Geoffrey's considerable task for a few days. However the time eventually arrived when any further procrastination was inexcusable. All newspaper duties had been met. Jane and children had been conveyed to Jane's parents for the summer holiday. He was a free man if only he did not have this research enquiry requested by Geoffrey Lancaster.

He stared at his list. How would he handle this research.

Initially he thought it might be wise to phone or write to prospective individuals and arrange interviews. However would not the interviews be flawed with opinions prepared beforehand. One might argue that such opinions might be of improved value with such fore thought. Either way it may stray radically from a spontaneous opinion. What was of greater value?

And regardless of hypothetical value, how true is that opinion. Mankind has painted a picture of himself, an individual of respectability and wisdom, which is far from true. The real accuracy of his thoughts is highly questionable. Visit any law court and listen to the evidence of witnesses to a crime. Often it is difficult to believe that all witnesses viewed the same incident because the evidence given is so contrary.

Yet all witnesses will insist that their evidence is the truth, and no doubt astonished to learn of evidence so contrary to their understanding. Quite possibly they would be further astonished to understand that possibly all witnesses told the truth but their interpretation of what was seen and heard differed enormously. Now remember that these witnesses have possibly had many months to think about the matter, and yet it is quite likely that some or all evidence is incorrect!

All kinds of influences affect our opinions, thoughts, and recollections. A witness may be concerned about his appearance, opinion, and thoughts, and revise his recollection to meet peer approval. And such revision may be made with minimal awareness. Past experiences, dislikes and likes, can seriously prejudice evidence again with minimal awareness or extreme awareness.

Physical experiences current and of the past can damage the credibility and value of evidence. For example our eyesight, smell, and hearing differ considerably. Our opinion of large and small, fast and slow, sweet and malodorous, obnoxious noise and solicitous quiet, gentle and drastic behavior, and so forth can cover the full range of imagination.

And then consider distinct prejudice very difficult for many to conceal. Particularly when such hostile thoughts are based on experiences difficult to forget. Yet often the experiences were trivial, unimportant, and should have been ignored.

Richard did not need to be reminded of the cruel dishonest editorials in national newspapers and magazines that portrayed opinions based on prejudice and hate. To be a responsible citizen, one had to be very cautious in accepting any opinion without careful thought and understanding.

Richard evaluated his own thoughts when voting for individuals and local measures in the past. How much thought was invested in his answers? True we are all expected to be responsible citizens but in reality how many of us are. For many a quick tick with minimal thought! What real value was there in these votes?

The conscientious reporter pondered and sighed. What strange creatures we truly were. Geoffrey Lancaster was very smart passing his problem into Richard's lap. A decision needed to be made and now.

The decision was made. He would tackle the exercise as if handling a conventional newspaper enquiry. Individuals would be chosen at random, the question given, and he would record both opinions and reaction.

The following day presented him with warm summer weather – perfect conditions to commence the enquiry, and for the man in the street to respond.

Country of Scams.

Richard Homes realized it is one thing to make a list of the perceived wrongs in the U.S. It was another thing to ascertain the thoughts of the man in the street, and possibly arrive at some kind of conclusion. He shared his problem with Justin Blake, another news reporter, and was fortunate to get an immediate lead.

"Say Richard. I think I know the ideal guy for you. I met him through playing rugby. He is British, possesses a Green Card, and has had some experiences that might interest you. His name is Peter Blackberry, and here is his phone number."

Richard wasted no time, made an appointment, and two days later entered Peter Blackberry's office. Peter's profession was Construction Cost Planning and Management, and there were architect and engineer plans lying on tables and hanging to surrounding walls. He looked up with a grin, shook hands, and mischievously announced.

"Welcome to the Cost Planning world. How many construction plans would you like to order?"

Richard laughed suggesting that reporters lack the necessary intelligence to understand construction planning, and then confirmed the purpose of his visit.

"Blake tells me that you had some interesting experiences when you first arrived in the US."

"Well I certainly considered they were thought provoking. Suggest you make yourself comfortable and I will be as brief as possible."

Peter, who could have been mistaken as a lecturer, rose from his work table, and commenced to speak as if addressing a college class. With a mischievous smile he commenced by introducing himself.

Peter Blackberry, eldest son of Bill and Mary, has been well brought up by his devoted parents despite living in a London borough working class area. The local elementary public schools, despite their shabbiness, stressed the extreme importance of good behavior – prudent advice such as *"to be seen but not heard"*– an understanding that kept the individual law abiding and a respected citizen of Great Britain.

Now Peter lived in the fine city of San Francisco, and was in learned discourse with a local citizen.

Charlie pursed his lips, and stared at Peter with distinct disapproval.

He was a character who clearly had heard something that did not agree with his thinking. I asked him with complete humility, because I was well brought up, to explain what was his problem.

"What´s wrong with that?"

Well maybe someone can tell me because I rarely come across any U.S citizen prepared to share his thoughts regarding anything that might be considered *"controversial"*. Sorry I´m wrong. Government employees, at least some, and in particular those unpleasant and oppressive creeps employed as so called law enforcement officers throughout this great nation are often quite verbose with their fabricated opinions and claims. But one cannot take any of these characters seriously. They just think the public is the servant of government, and people are designed to be pushed around– and the way things are going perhaps they are right!

Anyhow enough of my belly aching.

Why did I query quite indignantly? Charlie presumably has every democratic right to express disapproval if he so should desire. Blame it all on my upbringing. Before the Second World War, parents understood they had a responsibility in the upbringing of their children. Accordingly Peter Blackberry had the benefit of a father who advised his son that the greatest achievement in life was to be respected and valued by society. No mention was made of personal monetary wealth. And Peter had the good fortune to be reminded by his grandfather that one should assist others not so fortunate. Remember always Peter, grandfather confided, that any good turn will always result in appreciation and a positive response even though it might take many years. The tone of his voice dropped a little perhaps disappointed in a particular son`s lack of understanding of this excellent advice. What was emphasized and accepted was that an honest generous mind actively employed was a contented one.

At this very moment Peter Blackberry is perched on a high bar stool in a popular drinking hole in the Marina district – a rather precarious perch made increasingly uncertain through consuming highly healthy beer with other members of the San Francisco Rugby Club. The evening rugby practice had ended, and quite a number of dirty bruised individuals were recovering with the perfect remedy – beer.

The year is 1969. The drinking hole is no doubt typical of thousands of American pubs. Unlike the highly unique and entertaining British pubs, there is little unique or interesting in its cousin pub across the "puddle" – all have the similar sad sterile sameness with customers matching that unfortunate sterility. However as one might imagine, a pub full of excited rugby players is quite a different animal, and fortunately Peter has wisely chosen this pub for the current evening.

Mr Peter Blackberry, for those not acquainted, is an excellent example of British Exports, and unique because he does not constantly break down. As a young man, professionally ambitious and hard working, his commendable enthusiasm earned him export status to a Central African office in Lusaka Northern Rhodesia. The 1950 population at that time was about 100,000 – now possibly 1.5 to 2 million. A population explosion in a nation that has destroyed its past excellent economy, and has allowed criminal politicians siphoning off the nation's available wealth.

Unfortunately for Peter, hard work and ambition did not earn him future prosperity. The wise politicians of Great Britain decided to allow the local people run their country. An African country, possibly the richest per capita during the 1950s, became one of the poorest! The correct but very negative opinion of Mr Peter Blackberry regarding the country's future administration was never requested, and if sought no doubt would have been shoveled under one huge pile of coal in the Westminster basement of the Houses of Parliament.

So our Peter decided to emigrate to Canada – a thought that had existed in his mind some 15 years earlier – and Vancouver British Columbia was chosen as his new home. However before his arrival some very curious Canadian Immigration officers in Montreal asked Peter why he was entering Canada at the commencement of the Canadian winter – the USA would be a much better bet! Indignantly our hero advised that he always wanted to live in Canada, and that enthusiastic loyalty and determination was apparently an adequate explanation for the puzzled officers.

After two years of hard work, our hero had to admit that perhaps Canadian Immigration had good reason for their recommendation. Many others in British Columbia also thought relocating to the south was a great idea. Little business involving his professional bent developed in the great province of British Columbia despite the vigorous lumber industry. Finally watching thousands of strong husky men idle six months every winter encouraged our man to look elsewhere. So now our traveler is located in the magical city of San Francisco. If Frank Sinatra could merely leave his heart in this fascinating city, Mr Blackberry was prepared to be far more generous – in fact he was prepared to offer his whole body although he had to admit no one had expressed any interest in this rather generous but questionable proposal.

That is enough of Mr Blackberry's life history – what else about this wanderer!

No doubt Bill and Mary Blackberry might take exception, but our assessment must be fair. Even writers have to be honest in respect of their critical readers who have shelled out a sizeable chunk of cash in order to inspect and consider the facts in written form. Thus we have the author's request that you are to read and assess the contents, and nod your noggins in full agreement of everything said and humbly request forgiveness for all that has been forgotten.

Mr Peter Blackberry, as you may imagine, in his early 30s is full of surplus energy currently invested or wasted on the great sport of Rugby Football. He is short on American standards say 5'8" provided he stands stiff upright. Weight is confidential, perhaps 125# - 135#, but not known because it costs 25 cents to weigh oneself. Hair dark brown, straight, and cut short. Eyes, like his Suffragette mother, a very firm grey blue with dark bushy eyebrows over. Facially nothing to swank about – just that typical rather serious concerned Blackberry look complete with an excellent healthy complexion and a big nose.

His health is truly A1 –The medical world would go bankrupt if it relied on a sick Mr Blackberry. He lives on vegetables and fruit – three of each daily as told by his Mum. She made it to 93 so she must be right. Dad a college professor of music obviously did not listen to Mum and departed straight to Heaven at the young age of 56. No doubt Dad's departure did not fit in with Mum's plans but resolutely she carried on in good health.

But don't fool yourself about these Blackberrys – there is far more than meets the casual eye. Examine our man's mouth. Firm, curls upwards with that faint evidence of a secret and confident smile. A smile ever ready to accept any kind of real humor, a smile that possesses secrets, and yet a smile coupled with a grin that will share humor and secrets with the right individual. There is clear evidence of stubborn fortitude and firm beliefs that will not change even if he is on the losing side. You might be tempted to introduce your pretty daughter to this character but might we suggest caution; there could be some recklessness in such an idea.

This evening we are unable to assess Blackberry's standard in dress – his taste in dirty rugby shorts and jersey is not commendable evidence. However we can assure the reader that our man commonly wears a high quality suit normally dark grey, white shirt, a tie representing his public school, and the finest leather shoes. Perfect appearance designed to give the impression of the successful business professional. Hopefully we may anticipate common sense and logic in any discourse overheard hereafter.

Charlie, the rugby club's right wing, is the current participant of a discussion of some concern, so a better understanding of this excellent gentleman is desirable. He is clearly valuable because he is the club's right wing but that is not adequate evidence for getting a bank credit rating and other qualifications which may seem rather important for the desirable economic respect of American society. So here is the club's right wing currently seated in a San Francisco drinking hole. What else can we derive from a cursory inspection?

6'0" Plus, husky, lanky, strong, and healthy. It is understood that he undertook conventional school education with no claimed credentials. But then who needs education and credentials when everyday there are advertisements in the paper offering $50,000 annually for a conventional salesman prepared to drive perhaps 40,000 miles annually. Of course such an occupation is naturally inconvenient whilst committed to Rugby, Baseball, Tennis, Swimming, and Girls. There simply is no spare time.

He is quite handsome, wide forehead, large clear light blue eyes, strong mouth, and an engaging smile. His teeth are perfect and white. No doubt his dentist can thank the size of his bank account for Charlie's teeth. He is a great talker especially after a few beers. His eyes offer the impression of openness, but as the number of beers consumed increase, those eyes become rather hard, narrow, and heartless. So what else can be told of this rugby hunk. Nothing much I guess. Nothing is known of his occupation in the working world. The astute tend to be quiet and make no comment about this individual.

He is a just a typical young man with limited education and perhaps not particularly bright.

Anyhow we are not here to be critical of patrons, particularly in this fine watering hole complete with sociable friendly company, and a number of beers down the hatch. Possibly Charlie had downed at least four beers, and felt entitled by then, to put this weird tiresome Englishman back into his rabbit hole. His friendly face unchanged up to the fourth beer was beginning to be not so friendly, and was now undertaking a transformation through the stress of drinking the fifth. As he explained the following day to Bob Finch San Francisco's Rugby Club's regular hooker, what right had that pommy to criticize our fine California economy!

In fact what credentials had that Pommy to make unfriendly comments about anything!

A very interesting point that reflects the nature and character of our upbringing. Peter's society held firmly to the saying "Waste not, want not" His grandfather, despite being mayor of Lambeth, picked up nails and screws lying in the road, and carefully stored them in jars designed for that purpose. Peter was constantly reminded that there was a use for everything. Enter any English home and one was confronted with furniture and furnishings for the past 150 years. Everything was treasured. One simply did not throw away anything. Significantly one rarely bought anything other than necessities. Commonly the family accepted the obligation of looking after the less fortunate. And society in general recognized the extreme importance of basic and advanced education.

Charlie, very different, was the product of a nation of people who were becoming increasingly affluent and mobile. Although ownership of things was important, it was of modern products which were easily attainable, rather than retaining family possessions of the past. The desire to treasure the past rapidly faded, and it applied to people as well as things. The knowledge and skills of the past was rejected, replaced by modern transportation, communications, and ill thought policies and beliefs that appeared and disappeared without consideration and ever increasing speed.

No longer did generation after generation live in the same neighborhood. Now young might be occupied in some place thousands of miles away. No longer was the responsibility of the elderly considered a family affair – sadly the young shrugged off those responsibilities - commerce and very occasionally the state took over that role. Unfortunately Charlie's society has never recognized the value of education and it has suffered accordingly. Business is a profit motivated activity and it's stated occupation and specialty takes a secondary role.

Two individuals with completely different backgrounds might suggest a variation in thought, beliefs, and understanding. No doubt those variations would require a very thick book and would not address directly Mr Blackberry's unhappiness. The astute would immediately point out that the real problem appeared to be some unfortunate experiences realized by this specific individual seeking work.

Well to be perfectly fair to all parties involved, perhaps we should go over Peter Blackberry's claimed calamities, and then judicially and equitably arrive at a conclusion. Admittedly we have not the advantage of Charlie who has had five beers, but we will endeavor to do our best. I take a deep breath and think back. Why was I so dissatisfied with my experiences in California. And perhaps just as important could I explain my indignation pertinent to an unsympathetic Charlie.

Well. Let's start off with my opinion of Charlie because I think you will then better understand my dissatisfaction with my experiences in California. To be fair it is not Charlie's fault – it is the system that has created Charlie. Bluntly he is a spoilt and uneducated, and is typical of millions throughout the nation.

Back in Africa I recollect loud spoken offensive tourists completely unaware of their failings who gave the local population a very poor and unnecessary bad impression of the western world. American consulate employees thoughtlessly advised the local people that they should run their own affairs knowing full well their advice was sabotaging the current British administration. But what truly stuck in my mind was the sight of a ship crewman sanding down a wood rail in the Cape Town docks. There he was, a big heavy florid man, seated before the rail, and smoking a cigar! I could not believe my eyes. All my life I thought only millionaires could afford cigars, and yet in America an ordinary workman could puff away. How could he possibly afford such a luxury?

In London during the early years of my profession, I proudly purchased a Parker 51 – the ultimate pen at that time. A whole month of hard work and wages was invested in that treasured pen. And yet in California one or possibly two hours work would cover the pen's cost. Any dedicated writer could own a row of Parker 51s in his top pocket without giving the possessions any thought. One tottered out of Safeway with four full bags of groceries – the cost a few dollars. That would be a miracle in England still trying to recover from the 1939 war. And then there were the fast food drive up franchises – a great hamburger, fries, salad, and as many cups of coffee for less than one dollar. Anyone with minimal credentials and just about no education, could survive without blinking.

Observing their good fortune was pleasing. What was unfortunate was the behavior of some of these fortunate people, the lack of concern of others, and the harm caused to the world by their activities that was disturbing.

Regardless of American economics and behavior, I realized, seated in the Marina drinking hole, that I should be grateful and very fortunate. The gods were on my side. But despite my good fortune, I stared at Charlie with some distaste. No way did he realize how fortunate he was. And now on his fifth beer he clearly had decided to put this British Export in his place.

Thinking back I was very fortunate n Canada after leaving Africa. Winter had started when I took a room at Vancouver's Burrard Street YMCA. With little awareness of the significance of the oncoming winter, I placed an advertisement in the Vancouver newspaper, and within days had five offers! Two were from contractors in Prince George and three in Vancouver. My interest in Prince George 500 miles north of Vancouver was rapidly tempered with an announcement that the temperature had dropped to minus 40 in that distant city. With that kind of coldness, parked cars left exposed outside at night ended up with square wheels the following morning! Vancouver residents with friendly concern warned that I would risk a square head as well.

So finally I represented a Vancouver specialist contractor which undertook a variety of specialized trades mainly in universities and Pulp Mills. Did I know what a Pulp Mill was? I said I did and got the job. But confidentially what I thought was a Pulp Mill I discovered was simply an enormous kiln for timber waste. Anyhow I was fortunate to get a job that winter, and the opportunity to improve my understanding of pulp mills. It was also my first exposure to what I suspected was an American Scam.

The University of British Columbia had a troublesome problem with the swimming pool – the painted sides kept on failing. The University engineer was determined that disturbing failing would not continue. Accordingly he invited numerous companies to apply their products on the pool sides, and the finest product would be chosen for the pool's protection. Peter's company possessed a special cement finish guaranteed to withstand all moisture and adverse conditions, and a sample panel was applied to the pool side. Six months later it was announced that this special cement finish from Florida would solve the engineer's dilemma.

Now with this skilled investigation and remarkable conclusion completed, the good engineer naturally assumed that his problem had been resolved, and he proudly informed the University executives of his remarkable skills and judgment. Peter was just as impressed viewing a pool with a finish that was so white and perfect in the glare of the summer sun. Alas like so many good things, the final outcome can be a disappointment; and in some instances a distinct calamity. Perhaps about nine months passed, someone, no doubt a real fuss pot, complained of some kind of porridge floating on the pool. His complaint, being the product of a real complainer, was rightly placed by the engineer in the garbage can.

But then someone else noted some kind of porridge floating around the high diving board, and later that week there were two more negative observations questioned who was eating porridge, and why was left over porridge being chucked into the pool.

Angrily the University engineer studied these unreasonable and senseless complaints, and finally he decided that he had best check up before putting these complainers in their rightful place. Unhappily for the unfortunate engineer, his credentials for resolving the pool's problem were destroyed, and his desire to trace and submit his unhappiness about a failed special cement finish persisted for a very long time. Peter, by the time he learnt of this disaster, was located many many miles distant from Vancouver. However he suspected that the special cement finish and the all important liquid "X" which had to be added to the cement mix was one big scam. But in all fairness and fortunately for the good people in Florida, Peter's suspicion was not supported with any meaningful evidence.

The following year Peter was consultant for a San Francisco Investment company, and designed, built, and managed the Prince George Industrial Park. Perhaps it might be considered he was reckless because he risked both square wheels and a square head in Prince George. However it is such adventurous individuals that have been responsible for the opening up of the undeveloped wild North West Canada.

Hopefully that brief introductory explanation would be adequate. However Charlie demonstrated no appreciation of my success and recklessness in Canada, so I offer a knowing smile and gave him a meaningful long look. Charlie's eyes narrowed and screwed tight refusing to acknowledge my smile and confident stare. What a guy.

I generously gave him an opening and pass of the rugby ball the previous week. I could have just as easily scored that try but thought he would appreciate my generous move. Not one cent of appreciation. How ungrateful can a guy be?

Anyhow my experience in Africa coupled with my good fortune in Canada gave me some optimism getting business in California. With little thought I hopped into the car, and three days later I arrived in San Francisco. At the border whatever documents I had were adequate for the visit, and any question of an illegal emigrant entry was never addressed or considered. My luck continued because Jim, son of my Canadian client, had a house overlooking Sausalito. How lucky can one be! And how naïve can one be!

Charlie sniffed in obvious disapproval with me being an illegal foreign emigrant.

"Absolute disgrace."

Prudently I ignore Charlie's hostile indignant opinion, and continued oblivious of my good fortune of that time.

Jim was the handsome eldest son of my client in Canada; an individual who had everything. He participated in sport car racing, owned an expensive two seat Porsche, had a residence located on the hilly slopes of Sausalito overlooking the marina, a principal of his father's business in downtown San Francisco, and built and owned a ski lodge in Bear Valley. And to compliment all these possessions, his opinion about any matter was impressive and specific even if incorrect.

My memories of that time recollect crossing the Golden Gate Bridge so many times often concealed by the rolling coastal fogs which rose over the steep hills overlooking Sausalito; coastal fogs that rolled down late afternoons hiding the many sail boats anchored in the Bay facing this attractive small town. Sausalito was basically a bedroom suburb of San Francisco, but one often wondered if anyone actually worked in the city. Yes a bedroom suburb catering to young swinging prosperous individuals who appeared to be completely free of any concerns regarding money, possessions, and sexual freedom.

Jim certainly could be considered a keen participant in this sexual freedom, and there seemed a different young woman in bed every night of the week! Everyone seemed to congregate at the many busy pubs down by the marina early evening and returned to the hillside residences later. One inevitably wondered where all these people raised the cash to support their expensive lives. One matter was certain –

despite Jim´s generous provision of accommodation, it was obvious that I had no spare time idly sitting around Sausalito.

Within a few weeks I had an apartment in the Marina District close to the Palace of Fine Arts, and was ready and eager to ferret out a respectable living. First I placed an advert in the Wall Street Journal. The cost was enormous but my expectations were even greater. **What a scam.** Every response ignored or had no use for my skills and experience, and took the opportunity to make numerous offers of fast food franchises, land, mineral deposits, buildings, coins – in fact everything and anything seemed to be available, a bargain, an opportunity, and for sale. All expected Muggins to fork out large sums of money. But employment or business contracts were significant by their complete absence.

I scratched is head – that was a great disappointment. But my face demonstrated greater determination through that set back. The next move was pretty obvious –the making of many enquiries in the construction world with not a glimmer of interest to reward numerous office visits. I had imagined that property owners, architects, and contractors would be extremely interested in the benefits of construction cost planning and possess economic understanding of the nature and implications of any project. Sadly to my surprise, that anticipated interest never occurred. There were just glazed eyes and disinterest.

Then a newspaper advertisement took my attention - financial officers, brokers, salesmen required for Charles Schwab. I had a vision imagining a position of authority set behind a fine mahogany desk calculating financial empires for unknown clients and with some luck a small share for myself. My appointment was handled by an attractive young woman who´s eyes sparkled with enthusiasm envisaging the making of huge sales and earning enormous commissions. It was so easy – shares in weapon industries, fighter planes, war ship yards, and manufacturers of every conceivable product for aggressive use, were ever increasing in value. Any salesman could not help making a fortune selling such stock. I, in my innocence, never thought a pretty female could be so enamored with the thought of enormous fees. At least in that matter my education improved, but my business future remained rock bottom. Peter Blackberry could not imagine himself as a salesman promoting investment in products of death! The Schwab business was simply gambling with no meaningful purpose other than making money. **Just another scam.**

Selling real estate adjoining a private airstrip was the next exciting opportunity. Peter Blackberry drove 80 miles north to Sacramento and attended a crowded real estate meeting. It was my first experience meeting and listening to what one might term a super real estate property salesman. He was unbelievably credible and successful, and already had made a fortune (fortune inferred) selling building sites to individuals with their private planes. As I possessed a flying license obtained in British Columbia, at last I had discovered the perfect occupation. At the meeting there were three American Airline pilots who had had their services terminated through their airline's lack of business. They also were excited and had the advantage of living in Marin County in the Tiburon area where most people were quite wealthy.

Time passed by. The guaranteed leads of potential buyers never developed into reality. Finally Peter realized that it was **another Scam** – naïve real estate salesmen, like himself, were expected to buy one of the air strip building sites to demonstrate confidence in the project. Finding buyers was a very specialized field - particularly buyers who owned a plane and liked the weird idea of planes taking off and landing next to their front door! The promised leads from the real estate company were simply talk. American Airlines reemployed their three pilots, and Peter was again on his own – unemployed and disappointed. The ideal occupation and airport lay in dust.

What was the next move?

Before I could respond to that question Charlie interrupted. He knew someone who made a fortune selling real estate. And he played a strong hand with that argument.

"If my friend can make plenty of sales, why can't you?"

I stare at this character who actually plays in the same rugby team. Gosh his face was truly hostile. He had made a good point, but no doubt his friend did not suffer the immediate handicap of being a recent visitor in a strange country. I mention this handicap, declared gloomily that selling real estate seemed a problem, and that just about everything seemed to be a scam. Life was extremely disappointing. My disappointment raises no sympathy from this crumb. He glared at me and claimed.

"You Pommies are all soft –expect everything to be laid out on a plate"

That really irritated me, and I made my mind up that I would never pass the rugby ball to him. And it was then I responded real cool and cold.

"What's wrong with that?

I stare at him with hard grey blue eyes. It was a complicated question that was unexpected, beyond Charlie's ability to answer, and he shambled off.

The following week was wasted visiting a number of architectural practices. Some claimed to undertake their own cost planning, and with glazed eyes patiently waited for me to depart. They all knew far more than I did. It was not knowledge or skill that was required. Their secret was simply finding the right source and client. To heck with the design economic benefits for their clients through this so called valuable expertise in construction design economics. Fortunately despite these setbacks, there was always the rugby practice to keep me enthused with life. To my surprise a few days later a sober Charlie curiously advised me that I had not completed telling him of my experiences. So we relaxed and I completed my tale of woes.

The subject of finding work or a business was on my mind and concern all the time, and finally I brought up the subject at another Marina watering hole. Mike, a British citizen, with very vague credentials, but a passable rugby front row scrum forward, had a great suggestion. Well shall we say it sounded a great idea after a number of beers. He had a friend who was also British (that made the business seem a respectable established bet!) who had a company selling a patent liquid soap. He was unwell and had to return to England. Buy his stock dirt cheap and one could guarantee success. All one had to do was knock on house front doors and sell the whole lot. Mike agreed to give Peter a hand in selling.

The following day Mr Peter Blackberry decided that he would commence the business empire of soap distribution, employ plenty of helpers, and would administer his business empire in the office working out how much money he was making. Thinking back Peter realized that he did not truly understand the implications of the business. Thinking again Peter now reluctantly admits that he was not overly impressed with the British character who's business he was purchasing. Basically he was simply buying cartons and cartons of this unique cleaning material, and nothing else. Mike's friend shrugged off any question of a problem, and told Peter that this stock would only last a few days. The product sells like hot cakes.

Later that week the sick seller was in England for his health check up, and Peter and Mike had it all lock, stock, and barrel. It was arranged that they would start their sales promotion in Marine County two days later. That was the first set back. Where was Mike?

Charlie's face demonstrated a great smarmy grin as he listened to my unhappy tale. What a friend! What a guy! What a lousy right wing!

I jutted out my chin and decided to commence the selling campaign without the missing Mike. It was then even British Exports realize their limitations. No one wanted this unique soap, many resented a salesman's appearance in front of their mosquito gauze entry door, and some threatened to get the police. Then it started to rain. By lunchtime our hero was exhausted, wet, and momentarily defeated. The product had not sold like hot cakes. In fact nothing had been sold. Seated in a fast food Dennys franchise, I gloomily munched a hamburger, and decided that I had better contact the missing Mike. Ominously the missing Mike continued to remain a missing Mike, and finally this business empire builder realized he had been **subject to another scam** but this time it had cost him some valued money.

Years later, Peter's future wife eyed the many unused cartons of soap, and asked very pointedly what and why and the reason for these many cartons. Poor Peter was extremely embarrassed and cannot remember his explanation. Regardless the good wife was too smart to believe him.

Charlie laughed and laughed. There was no sympathy in those laughs. What a pal. What a guy. Bill, a friend who hung out with Charlie, also grinned.

Thinking over all these disastrous events – **all were scams** - and one can forgive our hero's simplistic perception of California, the land of promise for his fortune, to be an immense disappointment. And Charlie had responded rather unkindly by inferring that Pete's criticism was unreasonable.

"Have you tried the labor exchange?"

And he continued making unsympathetic suggestions.

"Why don´t you start a charter airline – you have got a license."

Peter nodded aware how impractical was his suggestion.

"The only jobs available in the papers were commission only."

Charlie stared at Peter with a superior smirk.

"What's wrong with that."

Peter shook his head – he just was not a salesman. But he knew that beggars should not be choosers, and inevitably he wondered if he had any right to complain.

Bill broke into the conversation, and addressed Charlie.

"Hey man. You can't talk. Look how we got taken by that Hunting Lodge scam last year. That membership cost us $100 each so we could hunt moose last winter. And when we arrived at the club's property we were denied entry cos that salesman had never registered us as members. No one knew that guy. If ever there was a scam it was that one."

Charlie stared hard, angry, and embarrassed with that unwelcome reminder of being taken by that scam. But Bill had more to say.

"Yeah there are plenty of scams. Last year a car salesman sold me a car insurance that was guaranteed to cover every possible repair. The front end collapsed and my claim was denied. My attorney found fine print that just about denied any possible claim. That sure was a scam.

And just talk to the old folk – constantly pestered by criminals who offer services that they don't need. Just check building sites, farms, and small companies employing desperate workers at wages well below minimum wage. Check the many businesses that purposely employ illegal immigrants because they can pay very very low wages with no benefits."

Bill was incredulous, and challenged Charlie to be realistic.

"Come off it. Who are you kidding Charlie - this country is full of scams."

Charlie, taken aback by this unexpected outburst, glumly walked out without making any further comment.

I look across at Bill and grinned.

"Like a beer?"

Later in the apartment I study the Wall Street Journal. If ever there was a scam, that paper was a prime example. Careful study inevitably concludes the paper is designed for gamblers and scam con artists. Editorials, general comment, and advertisements are addressed to the gullible greedy reader, and suggest and extol the opportunity and bargain in participation of the prescribed ventures. Oil, gas, minerals, diamonds, gold, coins, environmental generation and so much more is offered. Unproved mines with enormous reserves, participation in unproved business ventures, every possible kind of investment is available, and all that is required is your money.

Any suggestion of a possible scam is rejected. The offering is designed and submitted to intelligent readers. Any response and acceptance is a judgment call by intelligent people. My. My. That appears to excuse every conceivable scam. Every fabrication, every falsehood, every defective claim, however extreme is exonerated because a judgment call is involved.

One might imagine that government institutions were designed to protect the public from such criminal activities, but such thought would be most unwise. In fact some unkind and knowledgeable might claim that government itself is often a self perpetuating scam, so any expectation of protection is unrealistic.

I shake my head. It is the nature of the beast. Life is forever searching for the bargain; preferably the bunch of fruit within easy reach; our habit of ignoring our own little dishonesties because no one is aware and accordingly no harm is caused.

I stare at an advertisement in a paper designed for those who may be planning one day to retire. There is a beautiful scene of undeveloped land with lakes and mountains behind. It tells the reader that for a mere few dollars every month, one may retire on spacious acreage in peace and tranquility. It is a fantastic investment opportunity - the value of the land can only increase! Very few parcels are available. Take advantage before it is too late.

Such adverts apply to numerous tracts of land of questionable utility in every state. Such tracts are transformed through energetic land surveyors into the planned investment of residential retirement dreams of considerable value. The offering is truly the desired bargain and the natural dream of so many– that is why the advert caught my eye.

No one is around to stress the failings of such offerings. No mention is made of the lack of availability or the cost of water, power, sanitary drainage, modern utilities, communications, conventional access, roads, medical facilities, law enforcement, public transportation, and so many other features and services that are normally taken for granted. Common sense and wise consideration would deter the wise. But such concerns when raised are brushed aside – there is no problem. One is constantly reminded that this is a bargain opportunity that will never occur again. Thus the gullible dreamers become taxpaying owners of properties that will never be developed or occupied. Sadly they will eventually realize **that their dream has become a scam.**

Who are the dreamers taken in by these scams. They are generally working class with little wealth who work throughout their lives possessing such dreams. Dreams that will transform the drabness of their lives. Dreams which eventually face economic reality and disappointment.

Peter shook his head. It truly was a disgrace that society permitted these land retirement scams. But then his face colored remembering that he once possessed an East Oregon parcel of five acres which he had been obliged to accept in lieu of commission. He also had his dreams. After a few years, the family drove out to view this unknown real estate. True the land was close to nature, in fact much too close; the barren land overlooked a treeless barren creek, the surrounding land drab, and many many miles from the nearest habitation. One solitary shabby trailer stood alone with no evidence of water, power, communication, or sanitation. The only roads were winding dirt tracks that had not been maintained. Peter's wife stared at him, and very meaningfully said.

"Well Brains. Is this it?"

The return journey to civilization was quiet and very embarrassing.

The lecturer completed his talk, grinned, and asked.

"Any questions?"

Richard, who never dreamt that Peter would reveal so much valuable information regarding his unfortunate experiences, expressed his regret that Peter had so much bad luck. He was pleased to note that now Peter had established a business practicing his old profession. Regarding questions he had one question only.

"What would resolve these problem scams, and what would you do to solve this disgrace?"

Peter Blackberry shrugged. With some bitterness he remarked.

"Come off it Richard. This is a national crime permitted by Washington and Federal Government. What I have revealed to you is no secret. Everyone with knowledge and authority is aware, and nothing is done. Everyone with an ounce of intelligence is aware, and nothing is done. The crime is the product of the nation´s people. What can a penniless idiot like me do? I can shout and scream for ever. No one listens.

There is a general attitude that the man in the street is quite capable of making decisions, a defective understanding that is encouraged by general business, and accordingly regulations are commonly opposed."

The curious newspaper reporter pondered over Peter´s experiences. Certainly Peter was rather naïve with his expectations no doubt based on his past business history in Africa and Canada.

" I just sense there must be a solution. It seems such a waste of time and effort for individuals to be constantly subject to these scams. If society is unwilling to control these scams, it would seem desirable that at least newcomers to this country should receive adequate advice warning them of the dangers and failings of these scams."

A knowledgeable construction cost planner gazed at Richard with some scorn.

" Richard. I have suffered my apprenticeship entering and establishing my life in this strange country. No. I would not like anyone else to experience such disappointments, but I am certain that millions and millions will suffer.

Have I a solution? Not really because I am convinced that the problems of this country have been created by the people now and in the past. For any meaningful change would demand a complete change in their beliefs. Beliefs so often based on ignorance, greed, and prejudice. Without such change I cannot imagine a resolution."

Peter paused a moment – then made some significant observations addressing the perceived nature and cause of the American dilemma. The newspaper reporter departed from Peter´s small office thoughtfully with much on his mind.

Many years later Richard read the latest news. Bernard Madoff NASDAQ former chairman admitted that his investment operation for years had been fraudulent and simply one huge Ponzi scheme that paid returns to investors from existing capital or new capital paid by new investors. **$65 Billion** was owed to presumably knowledgeable investors – not simple minded dreamers. ***Now that was a scam!***

It seemed unbelievable that scams small and large abound in a nation that claims to be the leader of the Western World. Yet they exist and for good reason. Education in general is very poor. Education is not respected. A gut feeling about everything is quite adequate! Any lack of education can be compensated by gambling whether the ordinary man in the street or the executive; whether tickets for a lottery, the casinos, or stocks and shares in some crazy business investment.

This lack of education results in a nation that takes short cuts that eliminates consideration, thought, and skills. Even the professionals are guilty having similar attitudes. Wise planning, analysis, checking, inspection demands sound checking by others but is rarely undertaken if ever considered . Inspection and checking is brushed aside – it all costs money and unnecessary.

Newspaper headings regularly announce commercial and industrial disasters, and many months or years later an explanation so often due to lack of responsible checking. Enormous buildings and structures continue to suffer with such calamities, but the lack of inspection, analysis, and checking is never promoted.

And such attitude eliminating thought and skills applies to all facets of life. The necessary awareness of skilled planning and subsequent controlled accomplishment rarely exists. Life in the U.S is one huge gamble. Unfortunately few remember that gamblers never win.

A pile of apples.

Adam surveyed the apples with a practiced eye. Hundreds and hundreds of Jonagold many trays high were expertly displayed to demonstrate their ultimate in perfection and availability. The low price of 88 cents per pound was at least 25 cents cheaper than the neighboring Granny Smith, Honeycrisp, Gala, Red/Gold Delicious, and Fugi apples, and a dollar less than some optimistically over valued brands.

What else might be learnt or should be known as we push our grocery carts along the endless aisles surmounted by every conceivable commodity and their imaginative packaging. The practiced eye might declare that what the customer viewed is precisely what is desired, and the purchase subject to the experience and knowledge of its owner. But the knowledgeable would shake their heads – experience and knowledge is inevitably tempered by the providence of life – qualified by the abundance or lack of success, wealth, and security. Much may be learnt by watching Adam.

He is well aware of the pricing skills and quirks of the grocery manager. Pricing would seem a harmless and relatively passive activity – if the price too high no sales – price too low no profits. But there is also a frustrating feature being the nature of the beast –both vegetables and fruit deteriorate and need to be sold or should be sold within a specific time frame. It probably explains why the description of the grocery manager skills includes the ability to lift 75 pounds on a regular basis accompanied with his anticipated skills of addition and subtraction. Tons of over ripe fruit and rotting vegetables need to be discreetly removed from the shelves and replaced with products of a superior condition. Clearly an individual eyed by the discerning customers puffing and groaning under the stress of handling over ripeness and rot is unacceptable.

Naturally this puffing and groaning handling products of a questionable quality is also unacceptable in the eyes of federal authority personnel with the task supposedly to protect the public. However those in the know smile inwardly because the most important task obviously is the protection of the federal authority representative's employment and retirement check rather than the health of the customer. Regardless there is another avenue; a solution which involves the cooperation of the unique sector of the market – the bargain hunter.

Thus the skilled and practiced eye of the bargain hunter is tempted and drawn to eye the questionable goods, now offered at an attractive low price determined by the cunning grocery manager. Hopefully the less skilled bargain hunters will take both the good and the not so good. With some forethought, skill, and luck, very little puffing and groaning will be required. One may consider the solution acceptable subject to the wisdom of the customer, while others might consider it unreasonable to risk the health of the bargain hunter. Regardless it is a trivial matter for responsible government executives and politicians in Washington. These important individuals have far more important concerns attending to the needs of friendly vested interests found in the back rooms of the U.S House of Representatives.

In fairness it is natural for the vendor to minimize waste, and Adam would ruefully accept that he would also have similar intent. One has to survive in a very competitive world. He recollected his experience in the outdoor markets in the northern city of Leeds England. The grocery stalls displayed very attractive apples, and Adam eagerly commenced to place a few in a bag.

"What do you think you are doing? Them apples are for show."

An irate vendor seized the bag. The apples set out on display were returned for display only. Indignantly he collected fruit from under the stall, and handed them to an embarrassed customer. Examination of the bag revealed that the vendor had indeed minimized waste with a couple of bruised cut specimens!

Adam possesses the very necessary skilled and practiced eye of the bargain hunter. It is a feature that would have embarrassed him if apparent and known by others in years past. Now at a mature age, whatever that means, there is no embarrassment, and his skill is considered a very important and necessary factor for economic and physical survival. Social Security monthly payment is $1009.00. Rent and utilities consumes $825.00. The balance $184.00 covers the cost of health (medical, dental, sight, hearing), food, laundry, household cleaning, car, haircut, personal hygiene, television, radio, computer, telephone, clothing, shoes, donations to the Salvation Army and the like, transportation, the payment of traffic fines for infractions invented by dishonest police and supported by dishonest judiciary, and so much more.

Enough! Enough! Enough! It cannot be done you claim.

You are correct. But it is a problem that is commonplace in a country that is claimed to be the leader of the western world. It is a problem that is not discussed or acknowledged by a claimed god fearing nation. And it is a common problem faced by 45 million individuals or more subject to heartless debt collectors.

Adam looked over the apples with a knowledgeable eye. Six months old, 18 months old – one matter was certain they were not fresh picked. Careful inspection revealed the fresh firmness had deteriorated - the attractive bloom of recent picked fruit missing. Some had evidence of minor bruising and others of chemical preservation. But always there would be a few free of defects.   Adams eye and hands skillfully inspected the exposed fruit and selected these survivors.

Adam's mind was intent through both habit and need. Every Wednesday it was customary for the large grocery stores to revise their prices, offering low bargain prices for some products, bargains whereby the customer might hopefully be tempted to visit and purchase their weekly needs. Adam's needs were dictated to specific items, and both price and quality assisted in the determination of his choice. Fruit and vegetables always headed the list being the necessities for good health.

Despite the intensity of his inspection, he was suddenly aware that he had competition. A female hand had entered the scene selectively going through the available produce. Momentarily he held back through this unexpected intrusion aware that someone else shared a similar purpose and need. With approval he noted her skill and selection. Carefully he looked aside. She was perhaps 5´4", modestly dressed in good taste, fifty to sixty years of age, with fair hair swept back in a firm manner.

Aware of Adam's glance she smiled. It was a generous soft smile which persisted as Adam indicated with mock alarm that she would possibly take all the good apples. A knowledgeable observer might comment that she would have welcomed a further overture, that Adam was well aware of that feeling, and yet he moved on to complete his shopping without further word.

An astute observer might question his avoidance of human contact – life can offer wonderful opportunities. Yet life can be unreasonably short eliminating the possibility of these wonderful opportunities. A lack of feeling, a personal self interest, deliberate isolation without human warmth – a multitude of explanations no doubt apply. Perhaps unconsciously he was like the bruised and cut apple. And of course minimal funds dictates a need to be very prudent. Regardless one wonders what precisely makes this character tick.

If asked whilst wandering around the many aisles of the grocery store, Adam would have difficulty answering such a personal and penetrating question. In fact he would probably shrug incapable or unwilling to respond in a meaningful manner. What precisely makes him tick is complex and no doubt economic.

Perhaps a careful observation might provide an improved understanding of this puzzling character. Adam does not exactly strike the observer as a John Wayne, Gary Cooper, or Woodrow Wilson but then who does? On the other side of the coin he most definitely could not be connected to the millions of poverty stricken citizens seen lounging despondently in every town and city of this great nation which no doubt is a relief for this individual.

One might thus conclude that he is an example of the boring middle class that permeates society involved in some kind of questionable activity during daylight hours. Naturally it is understood by all that this activity, whatever its utility, is limited by the all important television programs every morning, afternoon, and evening.

But Adam is not typical of this rather useless middle class. He has never possessed a television set. Physically he is pretty insignificant – perhaps 66 or 67 inches vertically. Aesthetically not very handsome although his Mum might dispute that opinion. Weighing in at 120 to 130 pounds, he would be considered rather reckless to demonstrate unnecessary pugnacity. But muscles, size, and weight complete with a baseball hat, although common and highly acceptable by a democratic, lethargic, and tasteless middle class, does not portray our hero.

Commonly when wandering around University libraries, he is assumed to be a lecturer. Although the observer is mistaken he could be forgiven for the error. Adam's sharp grey blue eyes and firm mouth suggests evidence of intelligence, determination, and learning. He is in fact British, a Londoner, with a professional upbringing in engineering. He was fortunate to have parents who recognized their obligation to ensure that their son had the best of possible education only limited by their marked lack of wealth.

Education and determination were the building blocks of success in life, and Adam was an ideal disciple of that thinking. And that firm belief remained with our man many generations later. Interesting how upbringing by a family can have such a positive feature throughout an individual's life. Adam cannot claim that his business life was exactly as successful as he imagined or hoped. But he is honest, accepts his failings, and agrees that his optimism at times might be considered rather reckless by the more materially cautious. Wryly he accepts that he entered this world with nothing, and quite possibly he will depart leaving little material monetary evidence of his life activities. In the meantime he is still very active and still optimistic although he realizes that his beliefs are contrary to a nation that does not plan for the future. A nation of gamblers whether active in Wall Street stocks and shares, Las Vegas slot machines, race tracks, or poker. Any gambling activity is of interest if a fortune is possible.

As may be appreciated Adam's thinking tends to gravitate to his current economic condition. Any surplus money from his monthly SSI check after the studio apartment's rent and utilities has been paid is set aside for food. Meat, vegetables, fruit, bread and cereals. Today as he wandered down the vegetable aisles, he eyed products considered as necessities – onions (48 cents#), cabbage (50 cents#), broccoli (80 cents#), carrots (70 cents#), tomatoes (80/90 cents#), celery (80/100 cents stick), parsley and cilantro (50 cents bunch). The prices mentioned are in general reasonable but Adam never expects any specific store offer all items at this bargain price list. Thus regularly every Wednesday he surveys all grocery stores – generally his purchasing spree is achieved by visiting the stores of Safeway, Albertsons, Kings, and other ambitious companies determined to profit feeding the masses.

The reader enjoying an established long term well paid employment may sniff with some disdain – no way in the reader's mind would he deem to spend much time selecting products subject to the advertised prices. But it is thought provoking to learn that Adam with his knowledge shakes his head in bewilderment of his fellow people who have no idea what is a reasonable price. Thus the price of just about any commodity can range from a reasonable price level to twice, thrice, and even higher levels. Stores simply identify their products for a given section of society – the prices rise as the assumed wealth of society is perceived. Adam often shakes his head in disbelief wandering around a so called upscale grocery store. He is staring at identical products offered by other grocery stores yet the price so high. And so incredible that customers select these products without any concern of the price!

He entered the tree lined street at the rear of the store, and commenced to return to his small studio apartment. The sky was mainly overcast, damp, and cool. A slight breeze was a sharp reminder that Summer had already departed. Tree foliage now yellow and orange, with leaves falling to accompany the thick bed on the sidewalk - clear evidence of the approaching winter. Adam stiffened aware of the change in weather and the unwelcome cold. Although conscious that throughout his life the cold had never been a concern, yet now his body was increasingly aware of that very cold.

The bag of apples took his memory back 50 years at the time of his arrival in the U.S. Then the favored apple was Red Delicious which was well shaped, firm, crisp, with juice sharp and sweet. Now sadly the same attractive product is tasteless and like eating cardboard. And this fault seemed to apply to all apples. **Appearance was always important whilst quality in taste suffered.**

As the shopper turned the street corner and faced the low winter sun, his mind dwelt on the wonderful apples he experienced as a young man in England. The condition of the fruit was often quite poor but the quality was delicious. True the green grocer would tempt the buyer with products free of blemish, and then skillfully offload some of the sadder looking fruit with the good. And that would apply to all vegetables. Vegetables never experienced the beauty treatment provided in the U.S., and yet had a flavor ten times better than their U.S. cousins.

Adam suddenly realized that *"Appearance"* was the overwhelming feature of all products in the U.S. In fact it applied to everything, and so often *"Quality"* suffered. He remembered his disappointment wandering around the Rose Gardens in Portland. All bushes had been awarded winners of a past year. Perhaps only two or three bushes could be found with a desirable lovely perfume.

The appearance of the blooms was the determining factor, and all other features secondary. None compared to Grandfather's rose bushes 70 years past that had the most wonderful perfume which could be detected well away from the plants.

The flower displays at Colorado State University in recent years in appearance were excellent, but there was no perfume, no pollen seeking insects, and no birds. It was another ominous example that *"Quality"* had suffered for the sake of *"Appearance."*

Adam became depressed thinking of the past. The quality of life has deteriorated so much. It did not matter whether it was an agricultural product, a manufactured tool, appliance, automobile, or whatever. *"Appearance"* was the dominating factor, and *"Quality"*, (long life and utility) suffered.

Climbing the stairs to his apartment, he realized that *"Appearance"* dominated not only products but most frightening it applied to the social behavior of the human race. Appearance is now all important whether the body or clothing. Everyone has identical perfectly straight white teeth and presumably good eyesight and hearing. All wear what is considered conventional smart clothing, all have the same false fabricated grin, and all have eyes, often hard with greed, that display self interest only. Millions and millions of identical selfish individuals who spend fortunes improving their teeth, eyesight, hearing, and reshaping their bodies. The medical world makes a fortune meeting these unnecessary needs. Significantly not a single cent is invested in their minds.

The door unlocked, Adam entered his small studio single room apartment. He smiled grimly – even the landlord had invested in *"Appearance"*. Although obviously designed for a single person with electrical baseboard heating, the owner had installed a huge family size fireplace, a large refrigerator and freezer, a large dish washer, a large family size stove and oven, and a fine large laundry washer and dryer also appropriate for a family. Adam admitted that his initial viewing of the apartment was definitely favorable, and these family size appliances had swayed that opinion. **BUT what a deplorable waste.** He never used any of the appliances other than a hot plate and a couple of shelves in the refrigerator. And the question arose how often would a single tenant use these appliances if ever?

Adam was startled to hear an unexpected ring at the apartment entrance. Rising he discovered a middle aged man named Richard Homes a newspaper reporter who wondered if Adam could spare a few moments. The subject to be discussed was excessive waste. Adam hesitated a few seconds, realized his social obligation to respond, and invited Richard into the apartment.

" My name is Adam Forthright. Would you like some coffee?"

"Please – black thank you."

The two men seated at a fine solid dining table faced each other and smiled. After Richard commented favorably on Adam´s compact apartment, he explained the reason for his enquiry and concern.

"Waste can be identified everywhere. Poorly designed buildings result in excessive heat transfer. Irresponsible planning and use of water is the cause of excessive water consumption. Unnecessary commercial and retail excessive packaging is designed for appearance rather than for utility. The provision and disposal of single use plastic bags a garbage and health hazard. The disposal of unwanted vehicles, boats, appliances, and industrial waste is a major cause of litter. The irresponsible ownership and abandonment of real estate is both criminal and a national disgrace."

Richard purposely paused in order to emphasise his opening statement, and looked direct at Adam with a smile of expectation.

"I am hoping that you may have some thoughts regarding this concern."

Adam sat with chest pressed against the table edge listening intently to his unexpected visitor. It was so very rare for anyone to seek his opinion; so very rare to meet anyone that desired to discuss this terrible problem. Slowly he gathered his thoughts and spoke.

"You know Richard I cannot speak with any authority about your concerns but I must tell you of my thoughts resulting from my shopping at the local grocery store. Are you interested?"

"Please carry on."

"Well the root of the problem is society´s fixation on Appearance."

He looked across at a newspaper reporter who carefully concealed his thoughts. Adam realized that this statement was most unexpected, and a detailed explanation was necessary. For over thirty minutes Adam described his very recent observations and conclusion. Finally he asked Richard to respond.

"What do you think?"

"I think your conclusion is very significant – very very pertinent to the problem. Congratulations. Your advice is excellent. Now I have only one other question. What would you do to solve the problem?"

Adam Forthright blinked. He did not have an immediate answer.

"Richard. Solving that problem is not a simple exercise. Have you any ideas?"

Richard did not have any ideas, and explained that he was hoping to learn a solution through his interviews. Adam pondered over this impasse – and was intrigued.

"Tell you what young man. Come back next Monday afternoon."

The following week an enthusiastic reporter possessed information both unique and valuable. Adam´s unique solution ensured all social and economic issues would be decided by the people rather than the current corrupt Washington political process. But the solution would be subject to a very significant proviso - the quality of the decision making would hinge very much on much improved education whereby ignorance, greed and prejudice of the citizen would be replaced with understanding, equity, and compassion.

Seated at the kitchen table that evening with Jane his wife, Richard discussed Adam`s solution. Jane pursed her lips in thought, sighed, and declared with some emphasis.

"My dear. That solution will keep you busy for the rest of your life."

The Root of the Problem

"My Dear – look at that absurd human child."

Mrs Chimp raised her tired eyes. Eyes that had appraised so many human children of varying sizes, shapes, and cleanliness. Eyes that had seen it all over so many years. Eyes so bored. Miriam yawned.

"What for?" She demanded. *"That one has a dirty unwashed face just like the rest of them. It is disgusting. The human race should not be permitted to have children."*

Chuck, always the faithful and responsible husband, absorbed this tit bit of wisdom without comment, and continued to stare out at the viewing area. The scene beyond the glazed screen was partly obscured with sticky greasy marks, the evidence of excited young visitors and their many jabbing grubby fingers.

Thoughtfully he digested Miriam's learned opinion as he examined the parents of this uncontrolled precocious infant. Yes. Miriam as usual was correct. This couple should have never been permitted to have children.

The reader should be aware that this meeting of minds occurred at the Portland Oregon Zoo, and such events and shared opinions have taken place day after day for the past 35 years. One is not obligated to question the intelligence and conclusion of the occupants. Just examine their wise and patient faces which have seen it all. Their eyes understandably are lined, worn, and tired.

Their faces are expressionless and conceal hidden thoughts. Both thank their lucky stars that their lives are separated from that ill bred human world so incomprehensible that exists beyond the dirty plate glass window.

"My Dear – try one of these peanuts – the label claims they are organic."

Miriam faithful partner for many years nods in a resigned manner. The peanuts are acceptable although she suspects the organic claim is false. Those humans are such a bunch of rascals. Life for Miriam and Chuck differs very little from day to day. Mind you the number of zoo visitors has increased enormously. The population of Portland and State of Oregon has doubled, and politicians and an ignorant population claim it is progress. Unfortunately the so called progress involves significant changes for the worse. The quality of life in Oregon is dominated by ignorance, greed, selfishness, and a lack of wisdom, compassion and understanding.

Miriam turns and looks direct at Chuck.

"Alright Brains. What are you going to do to resolve this human problem?"

Chuck, trapped by this leading question, responded with considerable political skill. Diplomatically he announced.

"We have got to get to the root of problem."

Miriam has heard this kind of answer before. Without hesitation she demanded.

"Alright Genius. What is the root of the problem?"

Miriam eyed her genius lordship uneasily as he beckoned her to enter the rear annex with him. Still vivid in her memory was her mistaken endorsement of Chuck's cardboard sign advising the public that he and Miriam, like so many million others, were unemployed, not entitled to food stamps, and required urgent food assistance (preferably choice tropical fruit). She blushed and rubbed her nose. It had been so embarrassing - all those gaping idiots staring with vacant faces.

Chuck pointed at four enormous piles of newspapers all rising from floor to ceiling, many yellow, aged, and curled.

Miriam unimpressed shrugged with disgust. It was just a pile of moldering old newspapers that should have been trucked to a pulp mill ages ago. Her Chuck was an incurable collector of newspapers, a collector who would never part with a single copy. Grumpily she demanded.

"So What?"

Chuck, aware of her lack of enthusiasm and understanding, patiently explained.

"The problem my dear is that there are far too many humans. The World increase in population is completely out of control. The world is threatened with a major catastrophe."

Miriam unimpressed stared without comment as Chuck climbed onto a crate, stretched and reached out, and grabbed hold of about twenty newspapers. Carefully he returned to the concrete floor, and laid out the papers. Newspapers of the West Coast included the Portland Oregonian, Seattle Times, San Francisco Chronicle, and Los Angeles Times. The Central Region included the Denver Post, Kansas City Post, and St Louis Post Dispatch. Finally the East Coast included the Miami Herald, Atlanta Journal, Charleston Post & Courier, New York Times, Boston Globe, and Portland Maine Press Herald.

Chuck looked up at Miriam. Still unimpressed, she pointedly remarked.

"Why are you showing me all these smelly useless papers?"

Chuck shut his eyes, and frowned. How incomprehensible and difficult women can be. How very very frustrating. With deliberate emphasis he secured his spectacles in place, and with exaggerated patience explained.

"Some of these papers have critical data and information that needs to be understood by responsible intelligent humans."

Miriam sniffed and was not convinced. She had given up reading the biased rubbish churned out by most American city newspapers who were just paid lackeys of big business. Just the thought of the useless and harmful opinions of the Portland Oregonian made her feel sick. Everything that was wrong with Portland over the past thirty years could be attributed to a permissive paper that did not give a damn for the people and the land. The poisoning of the Willamette River, the numerous industrial sites recklessly polluted by past owners, the obvious favoring of vested interests in property zoning, and the irresponsible city expenditure of public revenues that lacked all evidence of competitive bidding and planning.

Chuck with the benefit of 35 years marriage did not require Miriam to voice her opinions – he could read her mind – and quietly continued.

"Yes. I know. So many papers are utter rubbish and the cause of considerable harm. However there are a few papers that are credible and their contents should be valued. For example here is an old issue of the New York Times which is truly a great newspaper."

Carefully he opened the paper, and selected a page ear marked with a red marker, and started to read aloud.

Population Control is Mandatory.

"Consider the enormous increase in the World Population:

1804		1 billion.
1927		2 billion
1974		4 billion
1999		6 billion
2027	estimated	8 billion

Currently the world population is **about 7 billion** – 2 to 3 billion are trying to survive, and 1 billion are undernourished. The problem - families are far too large.

Current World agriculture feeding 7 billion is a dangerous balancing act with no prudent and adequate cushion for crop failures and other disasters. It is irresponsible to imagine there will not be failures and disasters. Present human activity endangers the possibility of a constant climate so necessary for the satisfactory growth of crops.

The current world ecosystem is threatened and resources are becoming increasingly scarce. Experts consider that world sustainable agriculture with adequate reserves is probably sufficient for a world population of **4 to 5 billion** – certainly not the current 7 billion or more.

A well balanced society is not only concerned about mere survival. Individuals need to be valued and meaningfully employed. That is not possible in any country subject to excessive population. **This concern applies to the U.S.A.** Agriculture experts deem that agriculture resources are adequate only for 200 million - not the approaching 350 million. Evidence of the economic status of the average U.S .citizen indicates a nation incapable of providing acceptable living standards for many millions. 10 to 15 million are unemployed. 48 million survive on food stamps. 1 to 2 million individuals are observed on the streets every day of the year destitute and without any credible shelter.

An excessive population well exceeding a sustainable number creates a dangerous stress on the country's resources, facilities, and economy. Crime, high incarceration rates, poor affordable education, a lack of available health facilities for the poor, and the millions unemployed or working at minimum wage is evidence of a country lacking responsible *control and unable to provide the necessary facilities and services for its citizens. **To permit any form of population increase is guaranteeing disaster.***"

The print was increasingly obscured by stains. Chuck adjusted his spectacles, and checked to see Miriam's reaction to this dramatic information. To his absolute disgust he realized that he had been reading aloud to no one. Miriam was rocking slowly backwards and forwards fast asleep! What was the world coming to? He raised his voice and demanded aloud.

"What do you think."

There was no response. Chuck shook his head and pondered. Why was it that only he could foresee the future's dire dangers. It was so obvious that soon there would be no room for anyone to sit down. Every square foot of land would be occupied by humans standing only. Shoe sizes exceeding 8 would be considered unacceptable! And much worse there would be no space to grow bananas, peanuts, dates, bread fruit, and other desirable tropical delicacies.

Gloomily he read another headline. Saudi Arabia was deporting five million illegal emigrants. 12% of the Saudi population was unemployed. Millions of immigrants without approved documentation were trying to escape being apprehended. All over the world there were similar examples of large numbers who had illegally entered other countries seeking work and escape claimed hostility. Illegal emigrants from countries throughout Africa, the Middle East, and Asia incapable of providing acceptable living conditions.

And this catastrophe applied to the USA as well. There were 10 to 14 million illegal emigrants from Mexico and other countries throughout Central America and South America. Nothing had been done over the past thirty years to solve the problem. And yet in the USA there were 10 to 15 million unemployed citizens and over 45 million on food stamps. Each illegal emigrant family, probably about four million, was costing the U.S. taxpayer about $30,000 annually to support. Four million illegal families were possibly costing the nation $120,000,000,000 annually.

Yes. Somehow these idiotic humans have to realize they are destroying this world, and change their useless ways. Population control was the only solution, and it needed to be undertaken immediately.

With the root of the problem identified, Chuck was now decidedly hungry. It was time for lunch. Touching Miriam gently, he indicated it was time to visit the dining area. She raised an eye now aware that Chuck's lecture had ended, and declared.

"Chuck. You did not brush your hair this morning. You are a disgrace. If your Mum and Dad saw you this moment, they would shake their heads in despair."

No doubt appearances are considered important in life, and might explain the need of Chuck to brush his hair. But appearances are much less important than the need of the human race to comprehend and respond urgently to serious matters. Chuck and Miriam's future supply of bananas, peanuts, dates, fruit bread, and other tropical delicacies was in dire jeopardy subject to the illogical behavior of the human race. Chuck mumbled and grumbled, and was convinced that his unruly hair had nothing to do with the current problem. Later he returned to the enclosure grunting and groaning pushing their old fashioned bath on legs. Miriam eyes widened now aware that the bath was filled with soil with two sign boards labeled *"Keep Out"* and *"Stay Out"*.

"What is going on! What do you think you are doing with our bath?"

Chucks face indicated a husband undertaking a very responsible and important mission. Carefully he installed the bath exposed to the day's sun, and then explained.

"My dear. There is an emergency. Just learnt that zoo keeper Wally Acorn's wife has just had her seventh child. Soon every square foot of my garden will be trampled over by Acorn children. This bath will be our future garden for growing peanuts and bananas"

Chuck beamed with satisfaction – a future problem had been solved. But now there was another problem. Miriam shook her head wondered why men are permitted to think and lead.

"And where genius are we going to have our bath?

Whilst most living species are subject to natural predators, unfavorable climates, disease, and shorter life expectancies, the human population has minimized such factors. Now through human activity, life expectancy and its implications is well beyond the ability of the world to handle. The time has arrived for the human race to arrange a firm policy whereby sound population control is undertaken throughout the planet. It is extremely significant to understand that modern society through research and industry has seriously contributed to the ever increasing world population. Improved medicine, disease control, superior food, prevention of natural disasters, and other positive features, is of little benefit when the end result is an ever increasing population and world disaster.

For over three hours Richard Homes had wandered around the Portland Zoo. Although of modest size located on a hill side close to down town, it was extremely well designed and the lack of size was not apparent. As he stared at the many occupants, it seemed so absurd that one small segment of society devoted so much care and time concerned with animal life whilst another much larger segment of society was busy destroying animal life through activities dominated by wealth and power. What was the solution. Obviously a radical change in human nature is mandatory. But was that radical change even possible.

The steam locomotive entered the zoo station puffing and wheezing. A ticket was purchased, and Richard was conveyed down the hillside passing through deep canyons and steep tree and fern lined slopes. At the Rose Garden station, he left the train, and walked through the attractive gardens and tennis courts, and finally the quiet residential streets leading into the city.

The reporter reflected over his recent visit. What had he learnt. Was a solution possible or was mankind bent on destroying the world and itself?

Farmer Giles saves the World

Dick Brown was now a correspondent for the Kansas Daily News. After graduating with a degree in literature and economics, he discovered to his disgust that despite assurances that education was the secret of success, the only beneficiary was the economic prosperity of his overly expensive college. The nation, despite its economic might, was unable to offer any form of employment utilizing his valuable expertise. However he was a young man still full of optimism and finally obtained a minor position in the Kansas Daily News.

For all those city dwellers with hands untouched by native soil, no doubt his choice of employment, location, and limited remuneration would be viewed with some distaste. How could one enjoy the admiration of others with regard to one´s possessions – the latest car, the finest of clothes, in fact anything of material value. True we may respect their thoughts but hopefully realize there are far more important concerns and interests in this world.

Thus we return to Dick Brown who provides an important service to the community. Certainly his employment was not exactly the finest, and definitely his compensation heart breaking. But that does not reflect the value and importance of his work which is to assist people to think in a meaningful manner.

Unfortunately thinking in a meaningful manner seems unnecessary to the average citizen in the USA. Certainly some may be prepared to admit that their education lacks polish. In fact for many there may be scant evidence of the purpose of dedicated teaching. However the need of such education in order to think in a meaningful manner is rejected as unnecessary.

It is simply a matter of common sense and the good lord has given them plenty of that. **They believe what they wish to believe**. Any suggestion of possible ignorance, greed, and prejudice is rejected with justified scorn. And why not when one considers the acts, the omissions, and the opinions of country leaders.

President Ronald Reagon brilliantly solved the country´s economy by closing down the institutions housing the mentally sick; President George W. Bush dismissed the possibility of agreement with Iraq through dialogue by declaring war; President Barack Obama´s inaction and meaningless talk has simply left all nation problems unchanged; Chairman Federal Reserve Alan Greenspan and his crazy opinions and predictions offered no solution or improvement to economic conditions.

Anyhow in the eyes of dedicated Dick Brown, meaningful thinking is a very necessary ingredient in the making of wise decisions, and currently his concern is the agricultural industry. Some considerable research in library and newspaper archives improved his understanding of the Federal Government Department of Agriculture. Washington currently pays enormous sums every year to farmers in direct subsidies termed "farm income stabilization" via U.S. farm bills. These bills predate the economic turmoil of the Great Depression with the 1922 Grain Futures Act, the 1929 Agricultural Marketing Act, and the 1933 Agricultural Adjustment Act, and created the basic tradition of government support for the industry.

The U.S.D.A programs and services include the Agricultural Research Services (ARS) with the praiseworthy purpose of ensuring high quality safe food, assessing the nutritional needs of the U.S., sustaining competitive agricultural economy, enhancing natural resources base and environment, and providing economic opportunities for rural citizens and communities.

There is also the U.S.D.A. National Resources Conservation Service (NRCS), its purpose and primary focus the conservation of agricultural land, the survey of soils, and of water quality.

It is claimed that the Federal Government Agricultural subsidies are paid to farmers and agricultural business to supplement their income, manage the supply of agricultural commodities, and influence the cost and supply of such commodities. For the year 2009, the Federal Government Department of Agriculture's outlay was **$20 billion** comprising of **$15 billion** for the Farm Income Stabilization Program and **$5 billion** for Agricultural Resources and Services.

These many dry facts meant little to Dick. William Sanderson lecturer at the local college suggested it was imperative that Dick possess a sound understanding of the agricultural industry and the Federal Government's involvement. Then they should meet and William would provide some eye opening information that could be the basis of an interesting newspaper investigation.

William was an older man, scraggy and alert, sharp eyed with a determined countenance. Breakfast at the local Perkins restaurant provided an adequate quiet meeting venue for two men rather excited about their proposed discussion. After eggs, bacon, toast, marmalade, and coffee, William advised he had some interesting information. He looked up at Dick and smiled.

"Do you realize that 75% of all subsidies are awarded to the largest 10% of all farming corporations. Corporations that obviously require no subsidies at all. Now understand all these Federal Government subsidies are being provided to the entire industry in which the average farmer earns $70,000 to $100,000!

It is scandalous that government provides so many programs assisting the farming community when there is no evidence to support the claim that the farming community requires any financial assistance over and above what is available in the private sector."

Dick completely unaware of this unexpected information looked over the table with care. It seemed difficult to imagine the staid government giving away hard earned tax revenues to such undeserving and unqualified recipients. He screwed his eyes imagining a scenario as described by William that seemed unrealistic.

"Are you certain?"

William aware that Dick was hesitant came over strongly.

"Look man. Just think carefully.

Currently the farming community boasts of participating in hedge fund bets to help increase crop prices already far too high through subsidies. Whilst this criminal nonsense continues, the majority of the USA working nation is unemployed or earning minimum wages.

Do you realize that large farming corporations are being paid to grow crops that can be grown far cheaper abroad – crops such as corn, cotton, wheat, rice, soy bean, sugar and the like. Also they are being paid not to grow specific crops. Finally subsidies are being paid for dairy and beef products in a market that is saturated.

And whilst all this money is wasted, over 45 million individuals in the U.S. are desperate surviving on food stamps!

Just consider the crime of crops being exported to Third World countries under the pretence of Foreign Aid assistance that in fact are not required, and are the cause of the demise and economic destruction of foreign farmers in their very own countries. Washington has insisted that Food Aid shall be American grown crops shipped from U.S. despite foreign crops being available at a lower price. The economies of foreign countries and their agriculture industries suffer due to the greed of the U.S. agricultural industry.

Another matter of extreme seriousness is the department's failure in its obligation to address the conservation of agricultural land and the enhancement of the natural resources base and environment. Just examine carefully the nature and character of the nation's farms. The farming community has been permitted to create enormous sterile acreages reliant on artificial fertilizers, the destruction of valuable hedgerows and trees, the removal and destruction of surrounding habitat, and the elimination of alternate crop rotation. Consider the frightening drop of bee population and other important pollinating insects and birds through the deteriorating sterile condition of the agricultural habitat. Rivers have become sewers conveying agricultural pollutants. All this terrible harm is caused by farmers determined only to earn greater profits financed and supported by the Federal Government."

Dick reacted to the lecturer's observations. Did it make sense. Weakly he remarked that it seemed unbelievable but his lack of conviction was apparent. Glumly he ordered two more coffees, and William continued.

*"Another example of government waste is the U.S.D.A. Crop Insurance. It is provided to the agricultural community through Risk Management Agency (RMA) which oversees and administers this crop insurance program at a cost of **$4 billion**. Also the Federal Crop Insurance Corporation gives subsidies to cover the farmer's premiums at a further cost of **$1.7 billion**! Take note that all these undeserved gifts are provided by farmers earning $70,000 to $100,000 annually or more.*

*It is an absolute disgrace and the shame of this country that these undeserved subsidies are the cause of poverty to Third World farmers, and also the financing of unnecessary farming activities harmful to the environment. Just think Dick. Total crop subsidies in 2004 was **$8 billion**. Since then more subsidies have been legislated with a value of **$6 to $8 billion** for corn crops grown with the sole purpose of producing Ethanol. What is so criminal and inexplicable is that Ethanol can be purchased far cheaper in Brazil and other foreign countries."*

The knowledgeable lecturer sat back for a temporary rest. Opposite Dick was occupied making notes. Already the data appeared to make little sense. If the federal department's obligation was to address the conservation of agricultural land and the enhancement of the natural resources base and environment, how could William's information be explained. He raised his head with the intention of asking an explanation. However William raised a finger and his lecture continued.

"Unfortunately the harm caused by this inexplicable agricultural support and subsidies does not end. Consider now the considerable harm caused to this Nation and the World through the activities of major agricultural manufacturers such as Archer Daniels Midland, Monsanto, Cargill, and others. These extremely wealthy corporations have dominated and controlled much of agriculture through the supply of fertilizers, genetic engineering, and the monopoly of various crops. Soils have been poisoned and impoverished, water ways and oceans destroyed due to fertilizer run off, and natural food crops endangered through genetic engineering. These corporations with earnings of billions of dollars annually incredibly backed by government subsidies have caused terrible economic and environmental damage, and a reason for higher crop prices. The cost of this environmental damage is beyond comprehension. Only the major agricultural businesses benefit.

*Direct subsidies for promoting crops that can be acquired cheaper from other countries are another serious matter. There are also subsidies granted that encourage specific crops not to be grown, and have no regard to the economic needs of the recipients. Consumers in the U.S. are obliged to pay much higher price for these commodities. And in foreign countries the recipients of crops delivered at a price harmful to the price of local crops, the local farmers suffer poverty and their country loses the economic benefit of local agriculture. Consider the gravity of U.N. Development Program claims. These unnecessary farm subsidies cost poor countries $50 billion annually in lost agricultural exports and $24 billion in lost income, **and are a major obstacle for economic growth.***

Finally an extremely harmful factor caused by unnecessary excessive crops and the centralization of the agricultural industry activities is the production of waste the cause of major national pollution problems; wastes that in the past were returned to the land for its benefit. The nation's water courses and rivers have become huge sewers, and the oceans at the mouth of major rivers dead. And of course further major environmental harm is caused by the enormous transportation system now required for the distribution of agricultural products due to this centralization."

William abruptly ended. He had given more than enough concerns which should be addressed by this young reporter. Concerns that he thought needed a detailed explanation and a satisfactory resolution.

"Who is responsible?" demanded Dick.

The elderly lecturer shook his head meaningfully.

"Young man. Start earning your salary. There should be little difficulty finding the rascals."

Farmer Giles aged 40 to 50 years was a typical representative of the farming community. Leaning against the entry gate, his weather beaten countenance tanned and leathery, he expressed both interest and curiosity facing a young newspaper reporter who had just driven many miles along dusty country roads for this very appointment.

Farmer Giles had lived all his life on this farm. In fact his father, his grandfather, and his great grandfather had conducted their farming life in the same area. For good reason he felt he was a satisfactory representative of the farming community in the central region to provide this young man with whatever information was desired.

"Well Dick. You know whatever information you desire, so why don't you go ahead and ask your questions."

Dick smiled pleased to note Farmer Giles willingness to talk.

"I must congratulate you. You have a great set up here. First I think the newspaper readers will be very interested in the history of your family and business."

He shuffled his feet ready to talk about something which he had pride. But first he beckoned and invited Dick into a nearby barn and office. Inside he pointed at a number of pictures and photographs hanging on the wall.

"That rather poor looking man standing with his wife is my great grandfather. Picture was taken in 1927. The small shed behind them was their home. The horse and cart on the side their only conveyance and transport. They had settled on 40 acres uncultivated land. Although they had travelled from the East Coast just about penniless, they succeeded.

The next picture is my grandfather about 1955. He was recruited and sent to Europe during the second world war. With government assistance, he took a course in agriculture and acquired 500 acres. That John Deere tractor was one of the early post war products, and was employed in the growth of large crops required at that time. As the years passed by, he invested his profits in more land, more equipment, and built a fine farm house currently occupied by my father.

Dad took over the farm from grandfather in 1983. During the following twenty years the business expanded and he acquired an additional 5000 acres. Many of the barns now standing were built by him housing both products and equipment.

Now we are standing on a spread of 8500 acres. I built a new residence because Dad remained in grandfather's house. Over the past thirty years further equipment and improvements has been acquired suitable for the needs of modern crop practices.

We are not exceptional- probably a typical example throughout the nation. Determination and hard work is the major ingredient of our success. We are proud to be considered the backbone of the nation supported by our concerned government."

Dick looked around. The history of Farmer Giles family was an excellent example what can be achieved through hard work and determination. Through the barn door he could see a spacious residence of high quality with four garages. In front two fabulous pick up trucks that must have cost $55,000 each. A Cadillac could be seen behind an open garage door. Equipment within the barn must have cost millions of dollars.

"Gosh. You have some fine equipment."

The good farmer pleased to hear Dick's compliment spent the next fifteen minutes describing some of his equipment. He stressed the wisdom of purchasing the absolute best regardless of cost.

"Always get the best Dick – that's the way to avoid problems and down time. Probably about $10 million has been invested in agricultural equipment. Never regret good money for good equipment."

The man nodded acknowledging his claimed wisdom.

Dick wondered if he personally was being dishonest wondering if it was feasible to possess 8500 acres, two substantial residences, a number of luxurious vehicles, numerous farm structures and improvements, and agricultural equipment claimed to have cost about $10 million. All this and more through honest hard work only! Diplomatically he avoided a subject which regardless remained on his mind.

"You are very wise in getting the best of equipment. Unfortunately my newspaper does not practice such wisdom regarding reporter cars. Tell me. I understand that the farming community is well supported by the federal government. Is that correct?"

Giles appreciated Dick´s compliment and nodded enthusiastically.

"Sure they do for very good reason. The Feds realized the importance of agriculture back in the 1920´s and has continued to support us ever since. We were described at that time, and still considered the backbone of the nation. Naturally the Feds support us."

Dick Brown nodded. It certainly made sense for the federal government to support the agricultural industry, and he wrote down some notes for future reference. He then frowned and pointed at some newspaper cuttings.

"Do you think there will always be a need for federal government assistance? Will it always be required?"

The solid farmer´s face stiffened, his mouth much tighter, and his eyes narrowed. He was aware of a young reporter gazing around at considerable affluence whilst making a very telling observation. The tone of his voice visibly changed and hardened.

"You do not understand. Farming is a risky business. The country cannot afford to allow the farming community to fail. We are truly the backbone of the nation."

He sensed that this newspaper reporter was approaching dangerous shifting sands, and that it was time to change course. At that moment Dick was staring at what appeared a very fabulous setting wondering how this set up could possibly fail, and why the federal government would be concerned of such a risk. Rather abruptly and a changed demeanor, Farmer Giles advised that their discussion had ended. He had urgent matters that required his immediate attention.

The following day Dick phoned another farmer in the same area and made a similar request for an interview. To his surprise, this farmer was obviously aware that Dick had seen Farmer Giles the previous day.

"Sorry Mister. I'm busy. I reckon I can't tell you any more than you have already heard."

An abrupt click denoted the end of that communication.

The ever insistent phone rang in Dick Brown's office. William Sanderson was curious to learn what progress had been accomplished regarding federal government agricultural subsidies. Dick related his activities throughout the previous week. Ruefully he admitted that the farming community did not seem very anxious to discuss the subject of subsidies. Throughout the State, the farmed lands appeared very affluent with no evidence of business failure. It supported the economic wealth statistics of the farming community as given by William Sanderson.

What seemed rather significant was a general insistence that the federal government subsidies were necessary to support the claimed risk of farming. Any matter relating to the questionable immediate need of this economic support, the terrible damage to the environment, and the senseless economic damage caused to foreign countries was brushed aside or ignored.

William chuckled loudly hearing of Dick's indignation of the obvious prosperity of the farmers – accepted there was wisdom in the enormous investment of high quality agricultural equipment – but the large quality residences, the finest barns and storage facilities, the extremely expensive trucks, private vehicles and the like throughout the land suggested that the industry had plenty of surplus money. Still fresh in Dick's mind was Farmer Giles attractive wife waving from her beautiful Cadillac – ruefully he realized that she would not be very impressed with his old battered Chrysler.

The college lecturer listened carefully and reassured Dick that his research was very valuable.

"My friend – we have a common interest in the agricultural industry. I have already suggested that federal government subsidies were completely unnecessary, and

questioned why such subsidies continued year after year. The nature and character of the industry since the second world war is very different to conditions prior to the second world war.

Yet I stress these subsidies continue. I imagine that any demanding newspaper correspondent, who realizes that there is no apparent sound reason for these subsidies, will seek an explanation. If there is no fair and responsible explanation, further enquiries may suggest dishonesty. Might I remind you that newspaper headlines constantly expose corruption involving Washington politicians, vested interests, and dishonest lobbyists. Perhaps an adequate explanation can be found in Washington."

Dick sat back in deep thought. He had just read a recent report in a business paper announcing that $11.3 million had been awarded to fifty billionaires over the period 1995 to 2012 that related to federal government agricultural subsidies. There appeared to be no end of beneficiaries.

He would have to undertake some research addressing the general wealth of the farming community. It should be quite a simple exercise. If the wealth is as described, it would be incredible to accept the claim that subsidies should continue to be granted to the farming community. Further research should reveal the parties involved in Washington. Their claimed concerns critically analysed, and their dishonesty revealed.

He suspected that there was little or no need of federal government economic assistance. The only service of value would be the strict administration and overseeing of regulations that addressed the nature and quality of safe food.

The private farming sector was quite capable of operating its business without any subsidies from the federal government. All farm subsidies needed to be abolished immediately. If the farming community desired crop insurance, it could obtain the risk coverage through the private sector.

It was apparent that the federal government through the department of agriculture has not fulfilled its mandate, and it would be preferable that these responsibilities should be transferred to the States where local people could be held accountable under the constant review of a critical community. The State's cost of handling these responsibilities could be paid by the farming industry.

Legislation was required whereby agricultural activities were decentralized and all current environmental problems eliminated by the industry. Sustainable and integrated farming was required with alternate commodity crops, legumes, and pasture to make good the terrible damage already caused to U.S. land.

He was confident that he would garner all the necessary information and evidence to establish the truth. But there was one matter which he thought was far more important but he could not resolve.

How could the citizens of the claimed most successful country in the Western World permit these crimes without meaningful acknowledgment and protest.

Dick Brown related all of his experiences to Richard Homes subsequent to a convention meeting. He stressed his bewilderment – the impression of living in a country of people who do not think or act.

"Are U.S. citizens so brainwashed and apathetic that they are incapable of understanding and taking action! Individuals in foreign countries nothing like as sophisticated as the USA are ever ready acquainted and vocal on important matters. Why the silence in this strange country?"

Richard realized he had the same question on his mind, and Dick was seeking the very reason and solution that he was seeking. For perhaps two minutes there was silence. Richard stared dully. Was a response wise or needed? Slowly he responded with care.

"It seems to reflect the sad nature and character of mankind. We speak of high ideals but never remain true to them. Greed of wealth and power seems to dominate the human mind.

Perhaps a social and political system that recognizes the failings of man, and instigates sound controls that minimize the harm of poor decision making would be a step in the right direction."

Two very thoughtful newspaper reporters left the convention center aware of a major social and economic issue of extreme gravity. The waste of public money was a national scandal. Both men were very much aware that establishing a solution would be a complex task.

Waste Not, Want Not.

Oliver Greenwood, clerical employee of the city emergency services sighed. Life seemed rather boring. He searched the book store shelves hoping to find something exciting. Jaded eyes suddenly lit up. An intriguing title caught his eye *"Waste Not, Want Not".* The wise title directed his mind to past years.

Waste Not, Want Not. There is no better advice – advice that no doubt has been quoted many a time over the history of man. Oliver's grandfather a successful business man in London often reminded his grandson of that wise maxim, and illustrated his firm belief setting aside every rejected item for future use. And of course this advice applied to one's conduct regarding money.

Too often he was tempted to purchase some unimportant thing, and his planned acquisition of a major important item suffered accordingly. He had disobeyed grandfather's wisdom.

This very simplistic maxim *"Waste Not, Want Not"* applies to all economic conduct, whether the individual, or the largest economic enterprise in the world. This wisdom most definitely applied **to *the collection and the distribution of the nation's annual wealth.***

Browsing through the dusty mixed shelves of a local book seller, Oliver found a text addressing the nation's annual wealth and it's failing in the distribution of that wealth. Summarized the data was extremely disturbing.

The criminal spending of Our Tax Money

The funding of all major government departments should be examined in general terms by all with the purpose of ascertaining annual cost, its nature, character, utility, and possible duplication in other government agencies. Also determine costs attributed to defective and inequitable foreign policies including the unsolicited interference of foreign governments, vested interests and lobbyists, and political entities.

The citizen is given to understand that such government outlays are invested for the benefit of the people. It is submitted that claim is incorrect.

Cost savings will be given reflecting proposed changes that would resolve perceived defective government spending, and amend aggravated problems that have resulted directly or indirectly through this spending.

Finally the reader will be made aware of the annual cost savings for him and his family through these changes. Savings which could be credited to you in the form of federal tax reductions and improved public facilities and services.

You will be astonished –possibly shocked – to realize how the average citizen has been so easily duped and taken advantage by your representatives in Washington. We are examining irresponsible and defective government distribution and spending of the annual tax revenues – coerced by dishonest politicians and vested interests. Money seized from your pocket and wallet in the form of taxation of wages and sales taxes, which has been given to undeserving entities.

You shake your head in denial of responsibility. Well study carefully the many examples of wasteful spending and inequitable concessions in this text, and ask yourself:

- Did you approve of this government expenditure.
- Did you advise your political representative of your approval or disapproval.
- Did you understand the serious economic and environmental harm caused by this spending.
- Were you aware that through this spending, it has caused the loss of employment opportunities throughout the nation, the reason for minimum wages, the lack of public facilities, and quite possibly your shabby neighborhood.
- Are you aware of the economic significance of changing or eliminating inappropriate government programs, and the economic benefits of transferring some Federal programs to the States. Such changes would improve the process through local understanding and efficiency.
- Did you realize that many current government outlays are not only wasteful and environmentally unsound but indirectly are destroying the economic lives of people living in foreign lands affected by these unwise U.S. subsidies.
- Finally did you understand the extreme importance and your obligation to change and improve government decision making and policies whereby there will be a distinct economic improvement for you and your family.

Rightly you may cautiously question the accuracy of the cost statistics quoted in this text.

All economic data has been extracted from the Federal Government Outlay by Detailed Function prepared by the U.S. Office of Management and Budget 2009 (p.461).

It is both significant and extremely disturbing that the U.S. General Accounting Office (GAO) refuses to certify the Federal Government's own accounting books because the book keeping records are so poor! About 80% of all Government Departments and Agencies have the lowest rating for financial management, and auditors cannot arrive at an opinion of their financial statements. ***It is claimed that possibly 50 to 100 billion dollars or more is lost through government overpayments. (The Heritage Foundation).***

Can you imagine yourself as a small business entrepreneur operating with no evidence of competent management and cost control? Your cashiers give out incorrect change – clerks forget to invoice items sold – staff approve fraudulent claims – your accountant firm completely oblivious of your business failings!

Would you approve of a small business owner bribing politicians directly or indirectly for the purpose of obtaining business orders and preferential treatment such as protective subsidies? You are asked again –Do you approve!

It is quite possible that the reader will arrive at the conclusion that the Heritage Foundation was quite modest in their claim. You may not be an accomplished book keeper but regardless you are no doubt far more responsible than your Federal Government. Apparently even the IRS does not know how much it has collected in payroll taxes!

Anyhow that is enough government bashing. Let us consider the credibility of the author. How accurate are the cost statistics as quoted representing your contribution every year to support the nation's money box, and more important the beneficial cost savings to you and your family resulting from the proposed budget outlay savings.

The cost statistics are calculated on dividing the government department outlays by 150 million. It has been assumed that there are about 150 million taxpayers who in turn may be considered family units. The number is approximate – it may be 135 million or perhaps 165 million. Clearly neither the Federal Government or the writer can be relied on a firm accurate number. However in this exercise the assumed number is adequate to demonstrate the serious waste of public money as it applies to the typical individual taxpayer's wallet.

No accountants, book keepers, and ledgers are involved. The data as given is sufficient to warn you of the gravity of federal government distribution of tax revenues, and more important the cost to the individual taxpayer.

Our analysis of each Federal Government department spending is set out department by department (18) commencing with the Department of Agriculture. The total Federal Government Outlay (2009) is listed as **$3,998,000,000,000 ($4 Trillion). Each Taxpayer's contribution for this enormous sum is $26,650.00 annually.**

$4 Trillion and similar numbers are mind boggling. What is incredible is that despite handling this gigantic bag of cash, the US General Accounting Office (GAO) refuses to certify the Federal Government's own accounting because the book keeping records are so poor.

Yes. All taxpayers responsible and intelligent should be constantly reminded and be highly concerned about the irresponsible state of affairs because it is indicative that the Federal Government lacks economic control, and is incapable of handling the Nation's business in a responsible manner.

Now it must be understood that the listed annual outlays do not in general include current annual emergency and supplementary spending approved by Washington during the current year which can be considerable. The writer is not well acquainted with this information but will make reference to such spending.

For example the Department of National Defense Outlay is stated to be $1375 billion but that number does not reflect total outlays. Include current emergency and supplementary spending **and the total spending is between $1400 billion and $2000 billion.**

But the Outlay for Department of National Defense is not merely an isolated example of how Washington irresponsibly distributes the national annual wealth. Examine the following federal government records for 2000:

How Washington spent your money

Federal Department	2009 Outlay	Taxpayer Contribution
Agriculture	20 billion	$133.00
Community/Regional Development	28 billion	$187.00
Commerce/Housing	758 billion	$5,053.00
Education/Training	79 billion	$527.00
Energy	27 billion	$180.00
General Science/Space	31 billion	$207.00
General Government	22 billion	$147.00
Health	354 billion	$2,353.00
International Affairs	41 billion	$273.00
Income Security	520 billion	$3,466.00
Administration Justice	53 billion	$353.00
Medicare	431 billion	$2,873.00
Natural Resources	42 billion	$280.00
National Defense (including E & S spending)	2000 billion	$13,333.00
Social Security	681 billion	$4,533.00
Transportation	94 billion	$627.00
Veteran Benefits	97 billion	$647.00
Nett Interest (Federal Debt)	143 billion	$953.00

Rescuing our Wallet and the Nation's Future

Reviewing the budgets and total outlays for each Federal Government Department reveals numerous examples of wasteful government spending. Reducing this wasteful spending will improve the economic well being of this Nation and more important the working conditions and prosperity of all citizens, taxpayers and families. It will also encourage and assist individual savings and investment significantly lacking in this country, and promote long term economic growth.

Irresponsible government programs, policies, and spending inevitably harm the country's economy. Currently the spending authority has been centralized in Washington, with politicians, bureaucrats, lobbyists, and special interests holding hands determining the distribution and award of the country's annual taxation funds.

This cozy arrangement "controlling the Nation's piggy bank" has existed for many years at the expense of you and your family.

Politicians and bureaucrats and their employees have constantly favored non deserving special interest entities and constituents providing benefits that would not be available in the private sector. Every important section of public policy has been hijacked to the back rooms of Washington, the policy modified whilst working its way through a lobby infested bargaining process that has favored vested and regional interests only.

Of course this inevitably encourages dishonest transfers of enormous wealth. No wonder most political representatives are extremely wealthy. And of course regardless of the outlay and its supposed purpose, the individual taxpayer has been deprived of his rights. Public records rarely possess the clarity needed whereby the public can understand or even know the winners and the losers enacted through the various legislative actions.

For example who truly understands the economic impact of climate change due to thoughtless decision making in connection with generating electricity. What is the true cost of generating electricity? Why has Washington not controlled the emissions of generating stations, industrial facilities, and the like.

Who has tried to understand the enormous harm providing subsidies to farmers resulting in terrible damage to the Nation's environment and considerable harm to foreign farmers and the economy of their country. Subsidies for local agriculture crops which can be grown far cheaper elsewhere in the world. What is the real cost of Ethanol and the actual damage caused by excessive corn crops.

The endless injustice of Federal laws and law enforcement; the appalling concealment of harmful products through manufacturing processes; the hostility of health care coverage; the rape of the country of minerals, fisheries, and forests. The list is endless and all is permitted by all taxpayers!

Proposed National Budget Outlay Savings

Proposed Savings to Federal Government Department Programs and Services through cancellation, transfer to State or Private Sector, and improved Department efficiency.

Federal Department	2009 Outlay Saving	Taxpayer Saving
Agriculture	20 billion	$133.00
Community/Regional Development	14 billion	$ 94.00
Commerce/Housing	231 billion	$1,540.00
Education/Training	------------	----------
Energy	22 billion	$147.00
General Science/Space	31 billion	$207.00
General Government	11 billion	$73.00
Health	52 billion	$347.00
International Affairs	28 billion	$187.00
Income Security	26 billion	$173.00
Administration Justice	27 billion	$177.00
Medicare	86 billion	$573.00
Natural Resources	32 billion	$213.00
National Defense (incl E & S Spending)	1000 billion	$6,667.00
Social Security	34 billion	$227.00
Transportation	22 billion	$147.00
Veteran Benefits	5 billion	$ 33.00
Nett Interest (Federal Debt)	------------	----------

Yes – $11,000 or more can be saved annually by each individual taxpayer without any cost liability of the Taxpayer! BUT it requires the Taxpayers commitment to get the necessary changes made in the current Washington budget decision making.

Don't shake your head. Your commitment is expected by your family. You are supposed to be a man –not a mouse.

Now this reduction of Federal Government Department Outlays and the individual taxpayer savings realized through proposed changes are approximate subject to the nature and extent of the proposed changes. What is far more valuable indirectly, particularly for your children, is the resolving of the serious environmental and economic harm caused to the nation and world through defective federal government policies and programs.

The restoration of rivers, seas, land, and air is mandatory to overcome the terrible damage caused by agriculture, fishing, mining, energy generating industries, and other damaging operations and omissions.

The recovery of natural crops destroyed through unnecessary agricultural practices, excessive application of fertilizers, and the intensive growth of crops. And the economic recovery of foreign farms ruined by ill thought U.S. subsidized crops and the equally ill thought so called Free Trade practices.

A very obvious question is placing a value to the cost of making good the extensive environmental harm already caused by defective Federal Government policies, programs and subsidies. The answer is not satisfactory other than the sums involved are enormous. **And if changes do not take place the cost of making good the environmental harm will increase enormously, and that possibly such recovery will not even be possible. That may be the future faced by your children!**

Resolving the National Debt.

The total Federal Government Outlay (2009) is listed as **$3,998,000,000,000 ($4 Trillion).** This enormous outlay included the sum of **$143 billion** which represented interest payment for the outstanding National Debt. No allowance was made for the payment and reduction of the **$14 Trillion National Debt.**

The $14 Trillion National Debt must be and can only be eliminated through wise judicial imposition, collection and distribution of the nation's taxation wealth, the elimination of all government waste, and the immediate planned repayment of the debt's principal and interest.

<u>**The Problem:**</u>   **The Federal Government's total national debt 2009 was:**

- **$13,529,000,000,000. ($13.53 trillion).** Each individual taxpayer will have to pay **$90,200.00** to settle that small account.
- **$16,000,000,000,000. ($16.00 trillion plus) (included all State and Other Authority debts).**The individual taxpayer's obligation has now risen to **$106,666.00.**

The individual taxpayer paid $953.00 in 2009 just to pay for the federal government's interest payment of $143 billion. Take careful note – that $953.00 did not repay a single cent of the $13.53 trillion principal owed.

Anyone who thinks that this problem of national debt does not apply personally should think very carefully. Agreed you may be paying little or no federal taxes currently to the Federal Government. But as the nation's economy plunges with its lack of financial resources, it results in a much lower standard of living, inflation, lousy education and health standards, poor justice and law enforcement, rampant crime, inefficient public transportation, a poisoned and polluted environment, and so many other negative features that influence your quality of life.

So even if you are a penniless non contributing taxpayer you are still paying for the enormous national debt through inflation and a severe lowering of your living standards.

The national debt is most definitely a major problem.

*Washington politicians often voice their biased ill thought economic solutions relating to the national debt that either increase spending promoting unsubstantiated speculative business and unproved profit, or demand decreased spending and services generally at the expense of the lowly individual taxpayer and citizen. **The real problem and solution is never addressed.***

Consider the terrible damage caused by Washington – the deregulation of the nation's banks (W.G. Bush), the promotion of Free Trade (Bush and Bill Clinton), the current investment promotion proposing unproved economic expansion (Barack Obama). All are examples of defective ideas which have favored vested interests and caused considerable harm to the nation's economy.

The real problem is the irresponsible and criminal spending by Washington on defective policies and programs favoring special vested interests, and the nation permitting its government to mismanage its responsibilities.

Stimulus Packages are often presented by Washington as the solution but never address the real problem. Thus the claimed enlightened policies introduced by Bush, Clinton, and Obama have proved a failure.

These packages have never addressed the real problem. A problem that persists — **dishonest Washington politicians with their criminal programs and policies that favor vested interests to the detriment of the nation's economy and the people. Also the inefficient management of federal government departments of their responsibilities.**

John Maynard Keynes, a well respected economist in the 1930s, was famous for his thoughts pertinent to his economic theory "The General Theory of Employment, Interest, and Money" He advocated large scale public work programs which F.D. Roosevelt incorporated as part of the New Deal. These Stimulus Packages as described by Keynes were claimed to have been a success, but one wonders what the outcome would have been if the nation had not participated in the Second World War. Whether or not those programs would have continued long term to resolve the problems of that time is questionable. One matter is certain. **He would not have approved of Washington favoring vested interests to the detriment of the nation.**

It would be of interest to ask the respected economist if his theories would have resolved the nation's economy whilst a large percentage of the nation's annual wealth was frittered away on policies, programs, and subsidies favoring special interests, irresponsible aggressive foreign policies, and general government mismanagement.

No doubt he would agree that a successful national economy is reliant on a happy and contented work force. Would he anticipate such happiness and contentment possible with the knowledge that millions of manufacturing and service jobs have been exported to foreign countries, that possibly eight to eleven million or more unemployed, a workforce poorly paid suffering job instability, all due to a corrupt Washington political scene favoring the inequitable distribution of wealth.

Mr Keynes is not with us. With respect to his theory about Stimulus Packages, he would no doubt be the first to agree with regard to the nation's economy and the national debt:

- The waste of the nation's wealth on vested interests and aggressive foreign policies is detrimental to the economy and must be stopped.
- The mismanagement, dishonesty, and inefficiency of government departments must be resolved and improved.
- A nation without a meaningful representative political system that does not act in the interests of the people simply invites both political and economic disaster.

One matter is obvious. **The U.S is bankrupt, and the nation cannot afford to raise the national debt.**

This sad state of affairs cannot be resolved through the conventional political process in Washington. It cannot be trusted to make decisions that are not tainted with corrupt directions from biased vested interests.

A well planned and designed economy requires integrity and thought. It must possess the desire and ability to identify the economic implications of any proposed program, and if adopted, provide responsible management and cost control.

A sound satisfactory economy remains stable and safe, and creates a happy satisfied nation. With such a setting, the individual is valued and respected, and in turn his work is adequately rewarded and secure. When government expenditure and incoming revenues are balanced, profit generated by the economy can be well invested, and criminal aggressive and hostile foreign policies are rare or do not exist.

Washington politicians are not skilled economists or possess the skills and knowledge of the many government departments, and should never be permitted to enter the planning decision making process. They have been the prime cause of the Federal Debt, and their biased and irresponsible meddling in the process of economic decision making must be stopped.

The National Debt will be eliminated through wise judicial spending and the elimination of the prevalent government waste and inefficiency.

Under the earlier heading of **Budget Outlays – Money to be saved,** *a total annual saving of over* **$1.6 Trillion** *is proposed. The actual total savings could be more or less – regardless it is an enormous sum wasted on vested interests and inefficient government.*

This sum could be applied to reduce the $16 billion national debt. **Quite possibly responsible savings would eliminate the national debt within 15 to 20 years.**

The book was excellent. Now Oliver pondered over a personal economic decision. Whether he should or should not purchase the book. Discretely he examined the inside cover – the price $1.00. It was good value. Both the purchase and the text would have met grandfather's approval.

Grandfather would have approved of the elimination of waste in the Federal Government Annual Outlays and the settlement of the national debt. Most definitely he would be extremely concerned that the American people has permitted all decision making relating to the collection and distribution of the nation´s annual wealth in the hands of criminal dishonest politicians in Washington. Why do supposedly intelligent individuals allow complete inequity in the decision making process that excludes any meaningful inclusion of their concerns?

Whilst in the midst of making a major acquisition decision, Oliver was aware of another customer standing nearby in the same aisle, a customer now much closer, a customer overlooking his shoulder, a customer who suddenly remarked.

"That is an excellent book."

The stranger was referring to the text in Oliver´s possession. Oliver was intrigued, excited to meet someone with a shared interest, and made the obvious response.

"You have read it?"

"Certainly. That book should be on every book shelf in the country, in order to remind everyone what idiots they are being screwed by their politicians and the nation´s criminal companies."

The two men eyed each other and with some enthusiasm engaged themselves in a lengthy discussion of the book contents. The stranger introduced himself. He, Richard Homes newspaper reporter, was well read, and Oliver Greenwood was a transformed individual. He had found another individual with a common concern. However despite that pleasure he was startled to be reminded of his short coming in social responsibility.

" Oliver. We are discussing a prevalent problem that is destroying the nation´s economy and the quality of our lives. What do you suggest should be done to resolve it?"

"Well as you know it is a long term problem and the writer has clearly indicated the culprits. The system of making social and economic decisions has to be changed."

Oliver was aware that Richard absorbed this observation carefully with a quiet smile. With some discomfort and embarrassment he was asked.

"What would you do, or have done, to achieve these necessary changes?"

Thinking back Oliver was ashamed to admit that he had never considered doing anything, and what was worse he probably never would do anything. That newspaper reporter had revealed Oliver's weakness, and significantly the weakness of the American people.

Coffey Mugs take on the Future

View any street in this great country, and determined citizens are seen resolutely striding down the sidewalks. Admittedly that is not a remarkable observation, and probably applies to every country in the world. What is unique and strange about these particular citizens is their general demeanor and all are seen holding a coffee mug.

Your companion might impatiently remark "So What!" There are far more important subjects to discuss. But your companion is not correct and his response reflects the failure of not identifying a strange phenomena. Think back twenty years, and such a scene did not exist. Think back fifty to sixty years in gentile countries, and much has changed. Then it was correctly understood that to be seen in the street eating or drinking was considered unseemly!

Anyhow the subject of public eating, chewing, spitting, and drinking is not under review. What is of interest is this modern phenomenon of adult humans either singly but more often accompanied by others of a similar ilk making their way along public sidewalks. Throughout the nation's towns and cities, all possess an impression of self importance although their appearance might belie such opinion. Down the said sidewalk they stride with commendable purpose, an activity which many might consider of little significance.

What catches the observant eye is that all are holding a coffee mug, a receptacle held stiffly and balanced well ahead of its owner, an article that advertises the general presence of its important owner. Occasionally the subject pedestrians may share some confidence which one may suspect contains little of import. In general they are lower echelon office managers and employees, and the scene commonplace and harmless. Some are in suits clearly ready to undertake the decisions of the world. Others are more casual wearing tee shirts, wind breakers, and similar garments advertising a chain store, gas station, football team, or slogan, and of course wearing the proverbial baseball cap – they are all walking bill boards!

What is of interest is the cause of this strange happening, a social habit no doubt assisted and encouraged by Starbucks, and participated by millions of presumably fairly intelligent individuals male and female.

It is a question that defies explanation. Why should millions and millions of solid citizens suddenly adopt this strange and very public demonstration? Your companion may dampen your incredulity by stating that such strangeness in weird social habits is not remarkable. Perhaps he is correct. I remember visiting the Orinda Country Club during the late 1960s, and introduced to a professional supporter of Kennedy's political party. The man successfully imitated the appearance of the president with the distinct bend of the posture and an arm held behind the back, and immediately I was aware of an artificial political clone. The memory remained indelible and has been observed so many times thereafter of similar political clones. How strange individuals can be.

Very much like sheep they imitate each other. For some obscure reason, all feel compelled to copy and adopt strange activities and habits of their fellow people. It would appear perfectly harmless yet one wonders what precisely is going on between their two ears. Nothing! Well that could be very possible and an acceptable explanation. Others of course might argue that we all copy and adopt activities of others. Do we really understand this desire to imitate others? Or is this desire the product of a vacuum between two sprouting ears?

The problem is that so many popular activities and habits are of questionable value, and so often rapidly replaced by some other popular and meaningless trend. Any real evidence of thought and wisdom is significant by its absence.

During the 1960s I played tennis on the Vancouver park courts. The game was not particularly popular at that time, and there was little difficulty finding an available court. When I moved to San Francisco I continued the sport but vacant courts were difficult to find. Surprise - the tennis courts were overflowing with tennis players. The reason finally discovered was that tennis was now the sport to participate and be seen, and the masses accordingly took part. Every man was a budding Jimmy Connors. Every woman a gorgeous Gussy Moran. Now in later years, despite those praiseworthy ambitions, there is no difficulty finding a vacant court.

The next craze involved the absurd spectacle of individuals, many unseemly and overweight, seen pounding along the state freeways puffing and blowing. Presumably here was another great opportunity for the world to perceive Mister and Miss Athletic Fitness now participating in the healthy art of running. Everywhere men and women wearing their specialized running shoes would be observed transforming the nation's highways into running tracks. In their hundreds, often miles away from civilization, grimly and relentlessly they trundled with shirts advertising some credible organization of merit. Alas, like Julius Caesar, no longer are they seen. Presumably a finer way of presenting oneself to the world has been discovered.

You object to my questioning these praiseworthy occupations. Well perhaps you have good reason, but should we not be curious why such crazes take place. For example in recent years a large portion of the nation has decided that they must own fire arms. Gun owner associations have claimed that the need to own guns is for self defense. What is not mentioned is that accompanied with the increase in private ownership, more and more violent deaths occur. The greatest menace to society inevitably are the owners of fire arms and ignorance. Any meaningful thought and wisdom in this decision making is nonexistent. The question again is why the population emulate others and make these senseless decisions without good reason.

When a young boy, I recollect the general opinion that the well attired individual promoted alertness, understanding and wisdom. Untidy dress suggested and encouraged a lazy and ignorant mind. It might be argued that there are exceptions but why should the application of a sound opinion for the good of all be ignored for the benefit of the exceptions.

I remember remarking to the St Helens Oregon librarian that it was unfortunate that so much space and money had been invested in computers for the public, when it was obvious that so many machines were being used by individuals viewing pornography and comics. The librarian's response was immediate. She quoted one rare unique genius who apparently spent his whole school life watching and reading comics. Apparently because of this weird example, provision should be made for another possible unique genius, whilst the balance of society in St Helens suffered! I suggested that the objective of a library should be the education and entertainment of its readers. The disappointing deplorable choice of library books was unfortunate. Her response was similar to many other public libraries. *"Our selection is based on what our readers want!"*

Returning to the subject of dress and the choice decisions of many, the American college student is a fine example of imitation. Wander around any university and one has the pleasure of seeing thousands of young students desiring to understand their unique subject of choice. Despite the uniqueness of their study and no doubt the uniqueness of the student in the eyes of their proud parents, they all appear the same dressed slovenly with little evidence of laundry and iron. What seemed rather surprising was that the girls were often as untidy and disconnected as the young men, with little to identify the two sexes in appearance.

Most extraordinary as they lurched around the campus were the large rucksacks strapped to their shoulders presumably filled with dozens of study texts. Why was there the need to carry such a load of study material when presumably only one subject would be addressed in the typical lecture room. Why the choice of this rather unwieldy, unsightly, and uncomfortable method of carrying the required text materials.

Finally, and this seemed most strange, everyone conveyed a bottle holding their favored drink, which apparently was considered absolutely essential in order to survive the standard few hours on campus.   Thus drink containers are seen hanging and dangling on owner sides, connected to belts and rucksacks, set on their work tables, and constantly used to satisfy this strange necessary craving to drink.

What is going on?

Think back fifty years. It was recognized the need to dress and act smart to succeed. One's appearance was a reminder to be alert and conscious of one's obligations and expectations. To lurch around dressed in a slovenly manner was completely unacceptable. And under no circumstance would eating and drinking be permissible whilst in public gaze. And this behavior did not apply only to the executive and administrative world. Those in the army were reminded the necessity of being smart and alert.

What has caused all the students at the various colleges to act in a similar manner? I approached a small group of young men, pointed at their rucksacks, and asked why they were so popular. I never obtained a satisfactory explanation. Certainly I was advised that the rucksacks were used to convey their study material, but the reason for such large bags was not convincing. Whether or not the rucksack was an appropriate and convenient methodology for such conveyance simply produced vacant stares. The need of the water bottle also resulted in curious stares. Was I a reporter for some consumer organisation?

The question of dress was only addressed indirectly. I explained that years past students carried their needs in brief cases and similar items which were easy to handle and looked smart and businesslike. And it would be unacceptable to eat and drink in public areas. The young men stared at me with little comprehension – one suspected that they and I came from two different worlds. Why did they all think and act in a similar manner?

Admittedly one could have posed a similar question fifty years ago but then there was a recognized behavior set by society, and accordingly an acceptable explanation. Now there is no acceptable and intelligent explanation.

Any possible explanation and conclusion inevitably suggests that individuals act like sheep, and tend to copy each other with little thought. The desire to belong and be accepted within a specific group is apparent and suggests a need to be accepted and entertained.

It is rather disturbing to realize that when a group consists of many individuals who act like sheep, the possibility is minimal of a member promoting an idea, a policy, or program that differs considerably from current group thought.

Perhaps this act and the tendency to copy each other is comforting and provides individual needed confidence in a society that does not think. Regardless it is a state of affairs that can be detrimental in the making of wise decisions.

Richard Homes stood outside the entry foyer of Century Building, a typical high rise, with a popular coffee bar adjoining the main entrance. The time nearly 9 am and there was an endless troupe of workers entering the office building.

So many, male and female, were carrying the all important coffee mug held with due authority by its owner. It was quite amazing the proportion possessing this all important and necessary item. The newspaper reporter wisely refrained to ask any of these individuals why there was this need to acquire a mug of coffee. Most probably would be taken aback being questioned, stiffen, and make no comment.

And of course why should a citizen of the U.S. have to possess a reason for anything? Clearly if sinister newspaper reporters are wandering around making such impudent and irrelevant questions, there is clearly a need to invest 40 to 50 billion dollars annually in Homeland Security for protection!

The Rebel 51st State

Well past midnight, quiet and cool, the radio reception from a foreign station was excellent. Seated nearby the radio, Richard Homes concentrated absorbing a very detailed lecture about the Middle East. Dedicated to his vocation as a newspaper reporter, he realized the value of understanding the interpretation of events from a variety of sources. Inevitably all sources possessed inaccuracies and bias. However one had a far better and balanced understanding rather than relying on one source only.

The lecturer's subject was Palestine and the country's history over the past hundred years. Every now and then Richard would lean forward and write some notes for future reference. Initially the speaker made a curious and provocative observation, and then continued discussing past events to support his thinking.

Politicians, Historians, and Students rub their eyes. It is common knowledge that there are fifty States. Maps of North America are displayed, and all agree that this talk of a 51st State is baloney. The question is why this strange claim? What are the implications of this talk of an additional State and where is it located!

The difficulty in the USA is the unwillingness of claimed experts and leaders to accept evidence of past history. Thus the American Indian, after being totally exploited and often wiped out by early settlers, has had its existence conveniently swept under the carpet, and still awaits justice. Ancestors of the American Indian who walked or sailed across the North West from Asia have suffered general indifference until recent times. Columbus, incorrectly claimed to have been the first from Europe to discover America, rigidly holds sway in general American history books and opinion.

One might doubt the above. However when one realizes that even 3 years past, a supposedly intelligent professor at Colorado State University was still claiming that climate change was not caused by human activity. PLEASE! Any claim stupid and reckless can be expected in this country.

Yes. The accepted claim of there being fifty States in the USA is not disputed. What is suggested is that the activities of the National Security Agency which are slowly becoming unraveled is not the only disgrace committed and concealed by this country.

Foreign policy over the past one hundred years has been the shame of this nation dominated by economic and material gain rather than concern of mankind.

Enormous harm has been caused by corrupt politicians favoring vested interests with little or no consideration of the concerns of the nation and citizens whom they are supposed to represent. Greed, selfishness, material gain, and power are the prevalent and dominant factors.

A major cause of this corruption is the failing of the people, who have chosen democratic representation, to oversee and ensure that all decision making in Washington and other centers is equitable, democratic, and in their interest. Some acts and omissions such as pork barrel projects involve vested interests and benefit very small sectors of the population. Other policies and programs involve large vested groups such as the agricultural industries, affect national and world population physically and economically, and often apply and exist imposed for many years.

Finally there are policies and programs both advertised and concealed that address Free Trade, Immigration, Foreign Food Aid, and apply to the Nation's Foreign Policy which in turn is dominated by economic and material gain rather than the concern of mankind. Analysis of foreign policies over the past hundred years reveal the callous disregard of individual rights in the interference of foreign governments and their policies, the declaration of fabricated wars, and the invasion and occupation of foreign countries. Naked aggression rather than rational dialogue is the conventional policy. The final outcome years later is total failure of any meaningful benefit other than to specific commercial interests, and considerable harm to most individuals involved.

Throughout the world American senseless aggression is evident with armed forces and equipment, fortified embassies that emulate the ancient castles of old, unjustified interference with the rights of foreign countries, and a refusal to adopt rational dialogue to resolve disputes.

All this harm emanates from the activities and omissions of Washington.

Astute, devious and corrupt people have been aware of this weakness in the democratic process, and have taken full advantage as a group exerting mischievous and criminal political pressure on politicians. People, considered by some crazy and extreme, dedicated to possess and hold foreign land in the specific interest of their claimed religious beliefs. It is this corrupt group with compliant politicians that has created the illegal 51st State of U.S. within the lands of Palestine, seized a land that is now virtually a

Jewish prison, and has openly ignored the demands of United Nations to make good the ethnic cleansing of the expelled Arab population, the death of fifty to hundred thousand Arabs, and the theft of all Arab property in Palestine.

The claimed illegal State of Israel is in fact an armed camp of the U.S. strategically located in the center of the Middle East with the corrupt desire to dominate and control the oil supplies of that region. History describes the development and intent of this specific group of people with claimed religious beliefs, their callous hideous and barbaric activities over the past eighty years, ignoring the rights and concerns of innocent people, and the enormous burden and sacrifice now suffered by the American people.

During the period 8th and 14th century the Middle East was the cradle of scientific enquiry. The people of Mesopotamia have a remarkable record of scientific discoveries hundreds of years before Europe became aware of such knowledge. The Qurán encouraged science "God will raise up in rank those of you who have been given knowledge". The science of Medicine, Mathematics, Engineering, Astronomy, Optics, Chemistry, Physics, Cartography, and Evolutionary Theory was practiced whilst much of Europe remained oblivious and backward.

The land known now as Palestine has had two major populations for thousands of years – Arab and Jew. Both Arab and Jew have lived side by side with relative acceptance and understanding. The Jewish population was a small proportion of the total population mainly occupied in commerce whilst the Arab population was mainly involved in agriculture. Neither group actively interfered with each other. Both groups were mainly passive in nature.

The idea of a specific group of Jews, Zionist Jews, to have a home land began in the 19th century with the writings of Britain's prime minister Disraeli, and later in the century the thoughts and writing of Theodore Herzl who desired to emulate the success of Cecil Rhodes in Africa and considered the possibilities of Uganda, whilst during the first half of the 20th century the persistent diplomatic force of Chaim Weizmann favored Palestine.

It was remarkable how the Zionists infiltrated British political leadership, and indoctrinated notable leaders such as Balfour, Lloyd George, Churchill, Chamberlain, Ramsay MacDonald, Gilbert Clayton, Ronald Storrs, Henry MacMahon, Leopold Amery, Robert Cecil, and many others. And of course Arthur Balfour's declaration 1917 favoring a Jewish National Home in Palestine was a major coupe that resulted in thirty years of grief in the Middle East.

The future of Palestine in 1917 was postponed left as a mandate in the hands of Britain for a further thirty years. During that time nothing was resolved other than a repetition of ideas that had been dominated by Zionist thinking. The obvious conclusion would have been to recognize the natural rights of the Arabs in Palestine that would have check mated the grave danger of Zionist thinking and their crazy dangerous ideas.

The 1919 Paris Peace Conference perpetuated the conspiracy that a national home be established for the Jews in Palestine with the support, directly and indirectly, of the USA's President Woodrow Wilson. Just imagine. **The Muslim majority of Palestine, 80% to 90% of the population, who owned 94% of the land, was never consulted.** Their desire and natural rights for nationhood and independence totally ignored. It was an incredible state of affairs that continued another thirty years despite the Muslim majority demonstrating their unhappiness and resentment.

Gertrude Bell, possibly one of Britain's greatest in political intelligence and understanding, was incensed that politicians and Zionists at the Paris Conference would talk of Palestine as if the land was empty of people. **She predicted that the Arabs and Jews could not live peaceably side by side under the proposed arrangement**. It was significant that both she and the famous T.E. Lawrence and their considerable knowledge of the Middle East had no official standing at the Paris Conference.

Jewish people of a wide range of social standing also voiced their opposition. Sir Edward Montagu, Secretary of State for India declared that Zionism was a mischievous political creed untenable to loyal citizens of Britain. Lord Rothschild had his doubts. Many Jewish leaders believed that to offer Palestine to the Jews would be a disservice to Jewry. And many Jews settled in Palestine at that time dreaded the anticipated trouble that Zionism would cause to their future. Yet the narrow and selfish interests of USA and British politicians backed by Zionists continued unabated for the next thirty years.

When the Zionists realized that the British were possibly incapable of taking any action that would have met their approval, they astutely switched to the USA anticipating that their success could be achieved by encouraging the USA to pressure Britain, a country that was rapidly becoming economically bankrupt. It proved a brilliant strategy. In the USA there were about 4.6 million Jews of whom about 150,000 were Zionists. This small number acted as a voting block and basically blackmailed and bribed

USA politicians to make favorable Zionist announcements and resolutions at times of national elections. Thus Woodrow Wilson, Franklin Roosevelt, and Harry Truman all succumbed to Zionist pressures, and allowed local USA national issues and politics dominate the international scene in Palestine.

Zionists such as Rabbi Stephen Wise, Lewis Branes (Supreme Court Justice), Feliz Frankfurter (Harvard University), Henry Morganthau (Secretary Treasury), Harry Stimson (Secretary War), Summer Wells, and many others successfully infiltrated Washington by the 1940s. The membership of the American Palestine Committee included two thirds (66%) of the Senate, 200 members of the House of Representatives, the leaders of both major parties, and leading labor organizations. Both Roosevelt and Truman recognized the Jewish natural home to be Palestine. For both men that shared opinion 1944 and 1945 coincided with it being their election year!

In 1947 the decision regarding the fate of Palestine was in the hands of the United Nations. What took place demonstrated that any claimed democratic process determining national and international policies can be completely undemocratic, certainly not in the interest of the electorate, and only to the benefit of scoundrels and criminals.

Gertrude Bell an expert on the Middle East declared in the 1920s that any form of partition would be a failure.

Mahatme Ghandhi was very specific when he addressed the United Nations in 1947 regarding the proposed U.N.Partition.

"The Arabs could choose – not be forced – to give the Jews refuge, and it would have been a great generosity. The Jews did not have a right to the lands; It was the Arab´s decision to make, and they chose not to give the Jews land."

When Gandhi was asked what would be the most acceptable solution to the Palestinian problem, he declared.

"The abandonment wholly by the Jews of terrorism and other forms of violence."

It is difficult to believe that such injustice has taken place and committed by the most powerful countries and respected institutions in the world who all proclaim democracy. But of greater concern was the ever increasing malice, hate, aggression of the Jews made without any provocation. Despite the land being subject to a mandate with over hundred thousand British troops present responsible for peaceful administration and security, the intensity of criminal strife committed by local Jews increased.

The conduct of the British was puzzling and contrary. Sometimes they acted in the interest of the Arabs, yet other times very much against them. Arab protest had been treated with brutality, and Arab leaders were expelled from Palestine. Every act relating to the proposed partition was never for the benefit of the Arabs. And finally the British encouraged the immigration of European Jews to Palestine.

The Haganah, described a Hebrew defense force, was first established in 1920. Orde Wingate a British officer trained these men. 1936 He actively encouraged the Jewish settlers to be aggressive, trained them as troops to be more effective in attack and retaliation, and demonstrated how populations can be expelled and moved through military action involving the total destruction of villages and infra structure, and general brutality. Wingate was of a religious family which says little of such people. One of his men demonstrating the bestial efficiency of killing with bayonets to Haganah recruits was quoted to have sarcastically remarked.

"You men need to be educated."

The Jewish settlers proved good students. In 1941 the Zionist's military might was improved through the training of special commando units, the Palmach, who initially directed their efforts against the Germans. Later in 1944, their efforts were redirected to Palestine assisting in the formation of Jewish settlements. Large numbers of Jewish thugs were recruited from recent immigrants from Germany, Romania, and Poland.

The Irgun gang, an off shoot of the Haganah, founded in 1931 by the Zionists with the purpose of supporting militancy against the Arab population, was responsible for ever increased aggression and persecution throughout Palestine. Arms smuggling was discovered early 1933. In 1938 the Irgun killed 119 Palestinians. In 1940 this gang was led by Menachem Begin who would be a future Israel prime minister. Another extremely ruthless and vicious group was the Stern gang which split from the Irgun in 1940.

For thirty years the Zionists were responsible for murder, aggression, and persecution of the Arab population all over Palestine through gangs made up of unbelievably cruel characters with no respect for life or law. And it is significant to understand that the Haganah had an intelligence unit **founded in 1933** which was responsible in those early years for the sinister collection of information pertinent to the Arab people and their possessions, and comprised of a network of spies, informers, with collaborators throughout the whole of Palestine.

Careful surveys were made of every town and village gathering information invaluable for the elimination of Arab leaders, the seizure of real estate and personal property, the location of all water sources, minerals, agriculture, and aerial surveys that provided the vulnerability of such places when attacked by hostile forces.

This planned hostility spread against others. **1944/1945:** The British police headquarters was blown up, and seven British policemen murdered. **1946:** Six British soldiers were murdered. Nine British officers kidnapped and flogged. The King David Hotel was blown up and 91 British soldiers were killed. **1947:** The Jerusalem British Officers Club was attacked and twenty soldiers killed. Two British sergeants were hung, and their bodies booby trapped.

In Tel Aviv there is a building known as the "Red House" located on Yorkon Street close to the Mediterranean Sea. In **1946/1947** it became the headquarters of the Haganah. Within this building, Ben Gurion future prime minister of Israel had his office. There he planned with others the political future of the Zionist party, and designed a military machine whereby their political plans could be achieved regardless of equity and public opinion. Already the Zionists had received large stocks of arms, guns, mortars, and equipment from abroad. About 30,000 troops and 20,000 auxiliaries had been prepared for action. A planned squadron of Spitfires and naval support would be made available.

UNSCOP a United Nation committee for determining the future of Palestine initially favored a ten year period under some form of trusteeship, and yet finally caved in to Zionist pressure and recommended the partition of Palestine into two States. No one bothered to get the approval of the indigenous Arabs, and no one considered the consequences if the Palestinian Arabs disapproved of this inequitable decision.

The planned partition gave all the finest land to the Zionists including access to the two only Mediterranean ports, the main highways, railways, air, and communication systems. The remaining part of Palestine selected for the Palestinian Arabs was inferior, *fragmented, and much located in the hills. It was clear that the planned partition favored the Zionists in all matters of strategic importance and value.*

Finally 29th November 1947 U.N. passed General Assembly Resolution 181 which confirmed the recommendations of UNSCOP, and stressed that both States within Palestine must adhere to liberal democratic concepts.

Within one year in the presence of U.N observers 600 to 700 thousand Arabs had been expelled by the Jews, 500 to 600 villages destroyed, ten to twenty thousand Arabs died, and all Arab property stolen. *It was classic "Ethnic Cleansing" at its worst. Folke Bernedotte (U.N.) negotiated two truces during this period of persecution to no avail, and was assassinated by the Jews for his efforts.*

Ernest Bevin British Foreign Secretary was indignant that the Arab population which had occupied Palestine for more than twenty centuries should be expelled from their land and home to make way for another race, and claimed it was a profound injustice. He declared his astonishment that the conscience of the world was so little stirred by the tragedy of the Arab refugees. It was a disgrace that this tragedy had been planned and developed by Zionists pressuring political leaders in the USA to either approve their Zionist Jew requirements or suffer lack of their voter support in USA elections.

In 1948 the United Nation Assembly Resolution 217A (111) declared:

Article 9: No one shall be subjected to arbitrary arrest, detention, or exile.
Article 13/2: Everyone has the right to leave any country, including his own, and to return to his country.
Article 17/2: No one shall be arbitrarily deprived of his property.

For sixty years the terrorist State of Israel has ignored all U.N Resolutions. *During this period Palestine has been a Jewish prison subjected to illegal seizure of land, the constant persecution of the Arab community, and the death of thousands of Palestinians.* ***It is incredible that the USA, claimed democratic leader of the Western World, does not support and insist on Israel's compliance to United Nation Resolutions.***

*The USA has provided financial support of over **$3 billion** every year, and participated in the criminal charade of encouraging peace agreements between the Zionists and the Arabs. This charade has continued for over sixty years, and is a major* disgrace and the shame of the American people. Without question Israel is an armed USA camp set in the center of the Middle East with the purpose of dominating adjoining countries and controlling the production and supply of oil. Every day newspapers report of the deaths of Arab Palestinians attacked by Israeli army and settlers. How many more years will these crimes be permitted by the American people to continue?

Over **$3 billion taxpayers money** is used annually for this criminal purpose and the prevention of any form of democratic resolution regarding the theft of Palestinian land and property from the unfortunate Palestinian Arabs. What is so significant and tragic is that the brainwashed poverty stricken USA taxpayers continue to subsidise this illegal terrorist State. **It is incredible that these same brainwashed citizens permit their powerful democratic country deny adequate funds for their own poor, whilst such enormous sums are spent on a terrorist and illegal State in Palestine.**

Bluntly the taxpayer is financing a terrorist State at the expense of the rights of all people in this world, and has caused enormous harm to the stature and purpose of the United Nations. It is thought provoking that in this country people portray themselves as being democratic considerate god fearing creatures when the evidence is completely contrary to the facts as known.

"We believe what we want to believe."

So true. Beliefs so often based on ignorance, greed, and prejudice.

The lecture now complete, the program and station closed for the night. Richard rubbed his eyes. That was a long lecture but the information extremely valuable. It was an excellent example how the foreign policies of the USA were engineered meeting the interest of vested groups and their corrupt politicians in Washington.

The following day he decided to test the reaction of a few local citizens to some questions.

"Are you aware of the Ethnic Cleansing that took place in Palestine in 1948 which involved the expelling of about 700,000, the death of ten to twenty thousand, the theft of all their real estate and personal property. No compensation. No permission to return to their homeland?"

- John Black shook his head. He was not interested.
- Young man not identified. He had no time regarding an unimportant matter.
- Elderly lady at MacDonalds. She rapidly expressed her opinion with hate in her eyes. They (Arabs) were all scum!

"Did you know that Israel receives and has received over $3 billion annually from the USA. This money is your taxpayer money and supports a State that ignores United Nation Resolutions and continues to impose aggressive domination of the indigenous Arab population – a land that is virtually a Jewish prison?"

- Martin Bloomfield company director stared hard taking in the implications of the question, and asked *"Should I."* He walked on with no further comment.
- Jack Tate technician at a factory manufacturing weapons was more emphatic. He questioned if Richard was a true patriot. The weapons made by his company served a good purpose for USA security and his employment now and in the future.
- Marian Piper eyed Richard with concern. Yes she was aware of the problems in Palestine which were very upsetting. Her church had discussed the trouble a number of times. No the church had done nothing, and unfortunately she felt helpless. Should not Washington be responsible for changing its foreign policy.

"Are you aware of the terrible crimes and aggression taking place in Palestine. Many countries in the European Union are taking action against Israel. It is understandable that many Middle East countries are bitter about the disgraceful aggression of Israel and unwilling to do business. Would you be prepared to support action against Israel similar to that proposed by the European Union?"

- The president of a local university student union was very concerned. There had been many meetings at his college and also at other colleges throughout the nation. Yes meetings have taken place over many years with no meaningful result. Probably we should arrange a combined campaign with organizations in Europe. No he was stumped regarding an effective program that would persuade Israel adopt a civilized policy.
- Silas Manson dedicated Democratic was quite emphatic. Security of America was essential, and the world was full of terrorists intent in destroying America. Those brave Jews in Israel must be supported.
- Female manager of local bank listened to the question and gazed blankly. She simply requested to be excused.

- Gabriel Jacobson, an admitted Jew, would support action against Israel, and get rid of the Zionist Jews who were the shame of the Jewish people.

"Are you aware that Palestinian Arabs are being attacked and killed throughout Palestine by Jewish settlers in Israel. Israeli settlers were being encouraged to settle in the Western Bank creating increased hostility. These crimes take place whilst Israel pretends to undertake peace overtures with the Palestine State and ignores United Nation Resolutions. For over sixty years the USA has permitted and supported this criminal conduct?"

- Individual was unwilling to identify himself. Richard Homes newspaper reporter was completely misinformed. Palestine has always been the homeland of the Jews, and it is scandalous to be criticized defending their State from Arab terrorists. Israel has always supported peace overtures but the Arab people are bent on destruction. Clearly the USA is to be commended supporting Israel.
- An unemployed Alan Carter had difficulty understanding the question. No he was not acquainted with the troubles in the Middle East. He was much more concerned with his trouble finding work. No he had no idea how the problem could be solved, and bluntly he was not interested.
- Blake Sanderson was an employee in the defense industry. People had to understand that the USA is in peril from terrorist attacks. Israel must be defended as part of this country's defense strategy. Palestinian Arabs are forever causing trouble
- Those murderous Zionists are enemies of the world declared Mary Brown, and will be the cause of the Third World War. It is an absolute disgrace that the USA supports these ghastly people.

Richard pondered over the public response. The answers appeared adequate illustrating public understanding and prejudice. It was significant that despite extreme concern that even the most powerful groups resorted to words of protest only.

Climate Change – not Us

Los Altos is a most desirable and affluent neighborhood in the San Francisco Bay area. The public had been invited to attend an evening meeting at the local library arranged by the dynamic environmental group *"Keep the World clean and healthy."*

It was understood that the membership had undertaken an exhaustive investigation regarding climate change throughout the local community that included Palo Alto, Woodside, Mountain View, Sunnyvale, and Santa Clara, and various groups would report their findings. It should be noted that the inhabitants living within the areas investigated are relatively successful in business and quite wealthy when compared to residents in poorer areas. The data collected should be valuable and significant.

Oscar Peterson is president of the environmental group. His introduction is brief with the explanation that a number of members would be reporting their findings, and without any further delay he invited the representative of the first group to speak.

Gerald Moore rose to his feet accompanied with another three members of his group. Their investigation had addressed the excessive use of the automobile. Car ownership per family unit averaged two to four vehicles with one normally used by the head of the household for business. Many drove forty to fifty miles one way to an office located in the city. When asked if public transport had ever been considered, the response was a very negative shake of the head. The advantage of a non stressful journey by train whereby one could utilize valuable time just caused the incredulous citizen to stare. Urban sprawl created by absurd city planners was blamed by some for their residence located so far from work. No one was prepared to accept that their decision to live in these outward areas was due to cheap property. The three to four hour daily driving and the unnecessary cost was really none of our business.

The attractive wife of the head of the household confirmed that she had to own a car in order to undertake the necessary shopping, visit the medical world, entertain her friends, and other mandatory activities. She tossed her head indignantly. The necessity to use drive in facilities of banks, drug stores, and similar commercial activities was unquestionable; the possibility of using local public transport absolutely unacceptable.

The young man of the household was interviewed with some friends lounging around his car outside a fast food franchise. He had driven three miles to his chosen fast food outlet, spent ten to fifteen minutes in the drive up line, and of course would subsequently drive a further three miles returning home. He and his friends stared hard without comprehension when advised that their powerful 8 cylinder car had consumed at least ¾ gallon gasoline simply to purchase a hamburger. One companion, rather hostile, sneered that it was none of our business, and they would do as they wished.

Gerald Moore stressed how unfortunate that this kind of senseless activity is responsible for the burning of 9 billion gallons of gasoline annually, and a prime cause of climate change, national and world environmental pollution, and forthcoming natural weather caused disasters. Only a few generations past there was no such thing as drive up lines, and society was quite content to use their feet. It was very thought provoking why such facilities should be necessary. Gerald Moore´s group then visited the local high school where the young man interviewed attended. The parking lot was filled with hundreds of student driven cars. Any suggestion that these young local youths were physically capable of walking, running, or using the local bus was immediately rejected. Such suggestions were considered incredible. The claim that they were the cause of Climate Change was unacceptable –just a dismissive shrug.

The next group introduced to the audience had investigated truck freight transportation. Management of freight companies in Mountain View, Redwood City, and Sunnyvale was initially intrigued with their queries but that interest rapidly deteriorated to irritation when it was suggested that all long distant freight should be conveyed by rail. Such a suggestion threatened a very profitable business. Jack Taterson, unshaven and tired, complained demanding to know who would support his 19 drivers and families, his family, and who would compensate him for the loss of his business!

He was reminded that every interstate highway throughout the nation was filled with trucks travelling thousands of miles every month. **Well over 8 million freight trucks**! Highways and infra structures were being worn out, enormous amounts of fuel consumed, and trucking was responsible for a large portion of the nation´s environmental pollution. Trucks were commonly seen travelling speeds well exceeding national speed limits without being subject to any law enforcement. Jack Taterson was not receptive to changes. Presumably there were economic benefits delivering merchandise as fast as possible, and it was a subject not welcomed by trucking firms.

Finally everyone was aware of huge trucks parked, sometimes for hours, with their engines still operating. Drivers sometimes explained that if they shut down the engine, they would have considerable difficulty starting the engine again. No doubt an engine in excellent condition would not suffer this problem, but presumably that involved costs which the trucking company was not prepared to accept. Basically the trucking industry did not give a damn regarding the serious pollution caused. Profit consideration came before any form of public responsibility.

President Oscar Peterson thanked the group for their finding, and invited the audience for any comment. It was interesting to note that the subject of personal car usage was not raised by anyone. However two individuals raised astute observations regarding the trucking industry. Both realized the necessity for federal legislation instigating regulations that mandated long distant freight be conveyed by rail, with distribution only at rail points by trucking. How that legislation would be achieved was not explained.

The illegal disposal of unwanted vehicles, boats, and appliances was next addressed. Also the disposal of every conceivable product and waste material no longer required. It was a subject that required little discussion – the problem throughout the nation so obvious. The unwillingness and hostility of those responsible was a reminder that a significant number of the population was not willing to contribute solving this disposal problem. Some local authorities had offered incentives for the needed disposal and yet the problem persisted. The only solution proposed and supported by the audience was legislation that stipulated that all purchases should include a substantial financial bond to cover the cost of the eventual disposal.

The unwillingness and hostility of property owners liable and accountable for the proper stewardship of their real estate was another serious matter prevalent throughout the nation. Undeveloped land was often an environmental and health hazard, and the neglect of developed property often the cause of environmental harm, garbage, insanitary conditions, and crime. **There was a prevalent attitude that the property owner could do as he wished,** an attitude that often resulted in the unfortunate community suffering inconvenience, expense, and environmental harm.

The festering problem could be solved by imposing a finance bond on all properties to cover the cost of rectifying irresponsible owner management, maintenance, and abandonment. Regarding the economic burden of current mismanaged properties, the taxpaying community needed the authority to tax properties on the basis of best ultimate use, demand resolution of current problems, and if necessary the final option of compulsory seizure.

The irresponsible waste of energy consumed through excessive heat transfer and light of buildings generated considerable discussion. The investigating group revealed that residential and commercial buildings in the U.S. consumed 39% of the nation's primary energy. Industry and transportation consumed the balance. Much of this waste could be attributed to high heat transfer due to defective building planning, poor design and construction, and unsatisfactory operation and maintenance.

Although efficient and economic mechanical and electrical systems were an obvious solution, many property owners were unwilling to invest, particularly owners of properties leased to tenants who were liable for the buildings' operational cost. The solution - **legislation stipulating maximum levels of heat transfer of buildings and minimizing building energy consumption with strict government inspection for compliance.** Herbert Schwazerker owner of many local cheap apartment complexes objected – his tenants would not be able to afford the increased rents. It was not an economic argument sympathised or shared by the audience or by statistics elsewhere. The argument would have been evidence that the U.S. public was incapable and unwilling to resolve self created problems.

The time was well past 9.30pm. President Peterson thanked everyone for attending and reminded all that U.S. citizen accountability was essential for the solving of numerous environmental concerns. Many important topics had not been addressed such as excessive water consumption, excessive commercial and retail packaging, the abandonment and mismanagement of mining operations, and the harm caused by aggressive and destructive citizens. He thought it unfortunate that voluntary compliance to resolve individual wasteful habits had a patchy record. The solution for many major environmental problems was for the Federal Government to legislate responsible environmental standards that restricted or modified harmful practices, and impose heavy penalties for non compliance.

The forum participants and audience departed silently with thoughtful looks. Many problems and solutions had been identified. The question now arose – would such meetings organised by a few ever achieve any major national change through the current political process and the selfish interest of individuals and vested entities. And perhaps more significant these surveys had taken place in communities with residents of education and affluence. What would have been reaction of communities lacking this education and affluence?

One matter was certain – the U.S. citizen was very much responsible for the environmental ills of the world.

Richard Homes scratched his chin thoughtfully. There did not seem any advantage interviewing any of the environmental group members – the attitude of the general public in affluent sectors was pretty disheartening, and no doubt the attitude of less affluent people would differ little.

He examined his hand written notes made at the library, and shook his head. The habits, concern, and attitude of people in the USA was truly disturbing. No one truly cared, and no one had a positive solution other than expecting Federal Government in Washington to provide all necessary legislation to address current problems. No one suggested or cared how this so called legislation could be accomplished or imposed.

Private automobile use: No one was willing to admit their use the cause of energy waste and pollution – no one was prepared to give up their vehicle usage or use public transport.

Freight Transportation by Trucks: No way would freight company owners accept the obvious utility of long distance freight being handled by rail – regardless how polluting were their trucks, their wallet and profit was paramount. It was obvious that only Federal Government legislation could ever change a major cause of national and world environmental pollution.

Disposal of Junk: It was a country with a population that had very limited interest in controlling the ever increasing environmental damage caused by people who do not give a damn. The quality of life was so obviously damaged by these anti social individuals; and the guilt also applied to those who permitted their fellow people to behave in such a disgraceful manner. Everyone was basically guilty of a problem that was so totally unnecessary.

The Criminal Stewardship of Real Estate: Throughout the nation irresponsible use of real estate was apparent. Not only were the property owners guilty individuals – often large companies were just as irresponsible. Land and buildings were permitted to deteriorate, the land poisoned, encouraging environmental and criminal harm. Society suffered permitting this irresponsible conduct. Just consider the poisoning of the Willamette and Columbia Rivers by so called responsible Oregon corporations. All fish in polluted waters not to be eaten in a State which was supposedly famous for being environmentally attractive. What a lie. The polluting owners are permitted to do nothing. The low taxation penalty of vacant property permits this irresponsible conduct to continue.

Excessive Energy Transfer of Nation's Buildings: Viewing buildings in any town or city would not reveal the enormous environmental harm caused by these structures through loss of energy and inefficient heating and cooling systems. It is thought provoking that this ownership of property is obviously costing an unnecessary fortune, yet the owners do nothing and do not care because the cost of utilities has been bundled in the lease agreements with tenants. Legislation is the only solution.

Federal Government Legislation is Required: There is no argument that many major problems can only be resolved through federal government legislation because of individual unwillingness to change ways. BUT how can Washington be persuaded to enact legislation when subjected to the bribery of criminal vested entities and the persuasion of political constituents.

Richard pondered over his notes. True there are many who care and are concerned, and yet were handicapped unable to understand how the system could be changed. Change was mandatory but how could it be achieved?

Ruefully he remembered Galbraith's words of the late 1950's reflecting the product of uncontrolled progress. Sadly the writer described the typical family in their air conditioned automobile complete with the latest refinements traveling to the countryside for relaxation. It was a city of broken highways, garbage, deserted and mismanaged buildings, billboards and signs; a city lacking affection and pride. Then they would enter a countryside of polluted streams and rivers, garbage littered highways, and public areas of questionable health and safety. He naturally questioned the nature and character of mankind's genius that had been invested in this appalling progress.

Clearly it demonstrated a nation of people uneducated and lacking civic pride and concern. Yet within the nation there were pockets where irresponsible pollution was absent and civilized public conduct existed. Investigation revealed responsible leadership and laws controlled the behavior of all including those who lack civic pride and concern.

The required leadership and laws necessitated enforcement. Too many laws in the USA were never enforced. Richard remembered in California seeing so often a highway sign declaring a fine of $500.00 for litter, and sadly that sign would be surrounded with litter!

Education – still waiting for real change

Education is a subject most of us claim to understand. It is thus a puzzle that Education is such a failure in the USA. Thomas Wasterton screwed his eyes trying to understand this long standing common problem. Slowly he explained to a very patient and sympathetic newspaper reporter his observations.

I think back recollecting my education at a government elementary school in London before the second world war. The neighborhood was poor. My parents were poor. Regardless of the weather, we walked well over a mile shabbily dressed, with holes in socks and leaking shoes. Class student numbers were eighty or more taught by dedicated teachers. There was very little disobedience and all were educated.

Sadly I observed the very disappointing charade called education in Oregon, and my daughter's inability to understand simple multiplication. I explained to a teacher who was incapable of comprehending the methodology used at the London school. A methodology whereby we all learnt our multiplication tables in a poor school that had classes at least double the number of the Portland class. She just stared at me.

The nation's education system is poor, inefficient, costly, and inadequate for the needs of a modern society. The Federal Government despite making so many changes to the education system over the years has demonstrated a complete failure to resolve root problems. Essential improvements and changes have not taken place whilst education costs have increased with little control.

Basically the Federal Government has incorporated a straight jacket policy applied to all regardless whether the policy is appropriate or not. And it would appear that it lacks the intelligence, experience, will, and flexibility to make policy changes that would truly identify root problems.

Unfortunately the U.S. is a nation that does not respect intelligence. Money and power dominates the immediate thinking of the people. Thus the nature and character of needed education is rarely identified or supported. Changes, although many in number, have had very little utility.

What is rarely recognized is that we are all different. Our interests and our ability to learn differ. It is not a reflection of our intelligence. The education process must recognize this factor and identify the methodology necessary to raise the curiosity of the idle mind. We are all capable of learning.

Education with responsible upbringing should commence at a very young age. Without such education and upbringing at an early age, the child suffers a severe handicap often difficult to solve. Thus the importance of providing education facilities at a very young age.

College education costs have risen astronomically – rising far faster than the nation´s cost of living. It is common for the unfortunate student to be committed to education fees ranging from $50,000 to $150,000. Lending institutions are permitted to openly offer student financing at criminal rates of 30%. Yet the Federal Government Department of Education with full knowledge of these excessive fees and charges makes no effort to make education affordable.

A prevalent complaint of schools and colleges is lack of funding, the cause and the necessity to charge high fees. Any improvement of education standards is claimed not possible without increased funding. What is extremely distressing is that so many institutions are guilty of poor economic planning and the reckless spending on projects that have little or no educational value.

There are many issues to consider and implement including changes to current programs, the wise management and utilization of educational property, and the creation of an adequate trade school system:

- The Federal Government school lunch recipient program is highly commendable. However currently 25% to 35% of all families benefitting of this program are not in fact eligible due to their high income!

- There are a large number of programs that address the disabled (130), at risk youth (130), childhood development (90), international, cultural, and training exchange activities (75), employment and training programs (40), and K-12 School Grants (26). Most of these programs would be far better operated by the States or cancelled.

- Teachers are a great national asset and the finest must be employed. The teaching skills of fine teachers increase the value of every student in any community. The importance of employing the best teachers is essential. **An educational system that operates 12 months every year would encourage universal support for increased remuneration for education staff.**

- A well managed Trade School system is required in every State. As already discussed, simply because a student is not successful in the conventional school curriculum is not indicative that he or she is not intelligent. **Curiosity has to be aroused.** This was understood during the early 1900s in the U.K. At the age of 9 to 11 years, children sat for scholarship examinations. The successful progressed to grammar and public schools to matriculate at the age of 15 to 17, and possibly continued education in professional or university courses. But what was so important, the young school students of 9 to 11 years who failed the scholarship examination were transferred to Trade Schools, and obtained an excellent technical education. Many highly successful executives in business and industry attended these Trade and Polytechnic Schools.

- The management and utilization of school property is an important subject because it has a direct bearing on the cost of education. Most schools and colleges are vacant at least four months annually, and some six months. **Every facility should be open for education 12 months every year.** Every facility should be used both day and night, the evening classes possibly addressing adult education. The cost of the education of each student would drop dramatically.

- A factor that appears to be oblivious to all is the enormous acreage of school grounds enjoyed by each school facility which are unused most of the time. It makes sense that a specific school ground or school grounds should be shared and used by students of all age levels in the immediate area. And should not the school grounds be made available for the public as well. **The current status is a shocking waste of public money.**

- Another disturbing and unnecessary feature of cost at all schools and colleges is the extensive asphalt acreage provided for the automobile. All students should use public transport or their own legs. Parking areas should be limited to staff and commercial vehicles. **Another dreadful waste of public money.**

- Schools commonly lack secure management for much of the year and the facilities left to their fate. It is distressing to read of the unnecessary physical damage by vandals and destruction through inclement weather. **The obvious wisdom and economy of employing fulltime custodians living on the premises is so obvious.** And just as distressing is to read of school properties burnt to the ground due to a lack of an automatic fire sprinkler system. A common claim is the school district could not afford the cost of installing the sprinkler system.

- It is a ridiculous and reckless explanation because the cost of the fire sprinkler system is a very small part of the building's total cost. And that cost is recovered within a few years through lower insurance premiums.

- The expensive school bus systems must be eliminated. When possible public bus transportation systems should be used. Students should also be encouraged to walk and cycle.

- The problem of unpaid student education loans must be resolved. It is claimed that over 50% of all education student loans are in default with little or no hope of reimbursement. This nonsense requires to be stopped through rigid screening, guarantees, and immediate penalties applied against all defaulters. The interest rate financing of student loans by lending institutions must be limited to 10% or less.

With these changes, the cost of education per student will drop dramatically and the standard and quality of education rise.

Richard Homes congratulated Thomas for his excellent observations and solutions.

"Thomas. Your thoughts are excellent. Tell me how your solutions can be achieved."

Thomas was exasperated having to respond to a matter that should not have to be considered.

"This can only be achieved through meaningful legislation by the federal government. You need to work out some way of persuading those criminals in Washington to do the right thing."

The next interviewed was Jerry Henderson, one time High School hero in football circles until concussion ended his only vocation. He shook his head indicating his complete disagreement.

"You are dead wrong. There is nothing wrong with the system. My High School is considered one of the finest on the West Coast – has one of the best football teams and school bands."

Well concussion sadly can cloud individual thinking. American football should be banned from all schools. Jerry, with respect of his opinion, should be aware that American education is judged very low on international educational standards. And that should not be a surprise. The unfortunate students suffer very short terms made even shorter with teachers having the nerve to arrange meetings during school hours. And it is incredible that the school's unfortunate curriculum included students being taught to drive, to type, to participate in school bands, and other meaningless activities that had nothing to do with conventional basic education.

What was so amazing was that the quality and thinking of colleges and universities was little better than the schools. Many colleges like Colorado State University are more interested in providing services for the federal government related to U.S. aggression than to encourage education improving communication, understanding, goodwill, and compassion. Such research in activities pertinent to foreign interference and aggression is unwarranted and definitely not desirable. And of course university faculty employed in such undesirable activities are not available for their prime purpose of teaching students conventional civilized subjects. Another common problem is senior faculty travelling all over the world leaving the obligation of teaching to scholastic staff with limited education and skills. I remember one individual during the 1980s. He was often absent month after month travelling around Asia representing Nike. Obviously his students suffered a raw deal.

An extremely unsatisfactory state of affairs is universities who support athletic departments at an economic level far higher and at the expense of student departments. This is totally absurd particularly when universities such as Colorado State are forever demanding increased funding for student faculty. However when the president of Colorado State, which is claimed to be a secular college, openly supports a devious religion on the campus, what hope can be expected of sound policies and programs.

According to a report released recently by the Organisation of Economic Cooperation and Development (OECD) more than ten other developed

Western nations are already outpacing the U.S. in teaching their students the basic academic skills they need to compete in the 21st century global marketplace. Some degree of catch-up by previously less developed countries is natural, but the speed at which the skills of comparable developed countries are now outpacing the U.S. must be a matter of deep concern. Worse, unless the U.S. improves its faltering educational system, U.S. adults will fall further behind those of other countries. By international standards, despite a relatively high level of educational qualifications, the basic skills of adults in the United States are relatively weak. **American adults lag behind their peers in most other developed countries in mathematics, technology, and literacy.**

A recent editorial in the New York Times titled *"Why Other Countries Teach Better"* advised that job seekers were rapidly realizing that they suffered a major handicap competing against job seekers around the globe with comparable skills. The American work force has some of the weakest mathematical and problem solving skills in the developing world! To be competitive the skills of high performing countries can no longer be ignored.

It was thought provoking to acknowledge the superior education of Finland, a country that has the wisdom to have comprehensive schools that provide quality high standard education for both the poor and the wealthy. Also it is a country that provides hot meals, health and dental services, and family assistance.

The United States can either learn from its competitors abroad – and finally summon the will to make improvements – or fall further and further behind and suffer the economic consequences.

Richard concluded that national leadership was mandatory to achieve the needed changes. BUT how would it be achieved?

The Health Industry – Penny Wise, Shilling Foolish

Health standards in the U.S. compared to other western nations are poor whilst health costs are extremely high. A large part of the population has inadequate or no medical insurance, and health standards suffer accordingly.

The extremely high cost of medical and health care, the criminal cost of medical drugs, and medical insurance premiums that constantly rise, is very disturbing. No doubt the current situation reflects a nation suffering a multitude of economic and social problems – It is thought provoking and difficult to believe that the average citizen is reported to spend $6000 to $8000 annually on drugs alone! Even more disturbing the extraordinary high charges of medical and health care centers and practitioners.

The Medical and Health Industry in the U.S. has increased its charges for medical attention constantly for many years far exceeding the nation's annual cost of living index. There is very little evidence of the private sector controlling these spiraling costs, *and the end result numerous patients, often modestly affluent, are impoverished or even bankrupted despite possessing conventional medical insurance.* Yet despite these spiraling costs, the health industry often does not produce satisfactory results.

It is important to understand that the Medical and Health Industry is made up of many vested interests all profit motivated including hospitals, health centers, after care, doctors, surgeons, drug manufacturers and suppliers, emergency services, insurance companies, lawyers, real estate developers, design and construction, and others. The list of vested interests is enormous, and few desire any change to a very lucrative business.

It is incredible to read of patients being criminally charged thousands of dollars for merely stitching minor wounds in the emergency ward.

One cause for the prevalent high cost is because the medical and health industry constantly prescribe *"brand"* drugs when generic drugs of a similar quality are available at a much lower price. It is clear that this prescription of brand drugs is generated by the desire of profit. Thus the U.S. Industry callously persists in prescribing *"brand"* drugs whilst all developed countries in the Western World prescribe *"generic"* drugs which have similar performance and meet the economic needs of their patients.

Just think. Johnson & Johnson has agreed to pay the Federal Government **$2.2 billion ($2,200,000,000)** as settlement of allegations of the illegal promotion of **Risperdal.** One inevitably becomes aware that pharmaceutical companies must lack any form of ethical compass. Of course this callous attitude applies to the medical practitioners who prescribe the drug without thought or concern.

Do not imagine that the Johnson & Johnson matter is merely an isolated affair. **There have been numerous pharmaceutical companies that have been forced to write multi billion dollar checks to avoid prosecution and exclusion from participation in Federal Medicare and Medicaid reimbursement programs.**

Regulation of the drug industry should be enforced on Federal regulatory enforcement policies that are clear, with a process that is transparent, and on decisions that are accountable and reviewable, and that are congruent with other public policy imperatives.

Why does Health Care cost so much in the U.S.A.?

- It is obvious that the vested interests in the Health Industry do not desire any meaningful change that will upset their profit margin which is exorbitant.
- The administrative costs are astronomical – about 25% of health care costs is attributed to administrative costs. – much higher than any other country.
- U.S spends far more than other countries – for example cost of branded drugs.
- Americans demand and receive more medical care than people in other countries - so often a very expensive cure is chosen although it may not be required.
- The individual is not encouraged to make choices that are economically to their benefit – unnecessary services, pharmaceutical excessive charges, hidden and distorted information is prevalent.

Fortunately the Federal Government in the past has been concerned with the economic plight of those employed with modest means, and created the Social Security Insurance system whereby Medicare and Medicaid programs covered most of the cost of health care needs. However despite this excellent service, there are set deductibles to be paid by the patient. These set deductibles can represent considerable sums which truly penalise the poor. Also no paid healthcare service is available for examination and aids for eyes, teeth, hearing and other specialized features. Again such deductibles can be extremely expensive for the poor.

It is a praiseworthy and necessary service, but constantly subject to health care fraud. **It is difficult to understand or accept that it pays up to eight times the cost paid**

by other agencies for the same drugs and medical supplies. *One has the impression that the medical world considers Medicare an avenue to instant wealth.*

A very serious and constant problem is the amount of health care fraud, and the Department of Health's approval of high and excessive claims. For example one in five Medicare outpatients admitted to private hospitals is obliged to return to the hospital for further attention although initially the medical condition had been supposedly resolved! Apparently it is a great way to keep both hospital beds and hospital staff occupied and maintain a high income!

Other deplorable examples include a Texas doctor who has been charged with Medicare fraud involving $375 million committed in recent years. It is difficult to imagine government employees regularly authorizing these huge payments without adequate questioning but it happens!

Problems do not apply only to medical and health care. **The presence of tainted animal and vegetable products** is constantly discovered. Inevitably one wonders what kind of responsible checking is undertaken, if undertaken at all, by the Federal Government Food and Drug Administration to prevent these dangerous outbreaks.

And despite the Department of Health's research facilities, the public is constantly being reminded of disasters that should never have taken place. *Given the reason of an outbreak is of little value when the authority is incapable of identifying and preventing the problem initially.* The presence of formaldehyde in thousands of mobile home trailers made available for the homeless (The Katrina New Orleans disaster) by FEMA was a disgrace that should never have happened.

Health programs continue to consume more and more money yet do not produce satisfactory results.

Washington politicians constantly complain about the cost of Medicare and Medicaid, make futile and meaningless proposals, **but never make meaningful proposals to resolve core problems.** The Budget Office for example has suggested:

- A reduction of rates at which the Federal Government reimburses States.
- Reduce eligibility and number of mandatory services.
- Force beneficiaries to assume more medical costs.

Core problems never addressed by Washington or the Department of Health include:

- Irresponsible department low standards permitting fraud.
- Incorrect and omission of services that permit major health and financial problems to occur.
- A total lack of responsible management control and checks.
- The provision of adequate medical and health care for all citizens.

These root problems need to be resolved. Mandatory changes must include:

All HHS primary offices be held to the highest levels of integrity and reliability whereby their defined services are accomplished free of the many irresponsible problems that currently occur. **The heads of all departments must be held responsible and liable for all future errors and problems.**

Extremely high medical and health costs currently paid by the Department of Health for Medicare and Medicaid patients can be resolved by HHS determining a fair and reasonable rate for all procedures, services, and drugs, and to advise the private health industry that all members providing services to Medicare and Medicaid patients will be compensated according to these rates. This will assist in controlling excessive claims prevalent in the medical and healthcare industry but obviously will not stop medical fraud which can only be controlled by all departments held to the highest levels of integrity and reliability.

The very high Department of Health cost of managing Medicare and Medicaid compensation may be further reduced by providing all insurance recipients with vouchers to cover their cost of health services, and permit them make their own arrangements and decisions with the private medical and health sector.

Every individual in the nation should contribute to a national health insurance program whereby all may be entitled to appropriate medical and health care. All shall contribute according to their means whereby the nation´s total cost for healthcare shall be covered.

There does not appear any reason why the responsibilities of Health Research and Training should not be transferred to the Private Sector. The private sector with its wealthy institutions is more than capable of undertaking all necessary research and training.

Further mandatory changes may have to be adopted as follows:

Many western nations have national health schemes which provide excellent medical health services and avoid the economic disasters faced by patients in the U.S. All citizens contribute to the health system and a major financial problem is eliminated. However the U.S citizen and the Federal Government has made no concerted effort to resolve this problem. Presumably the private affluent sector is content with the current unsatisfactory health system.

However the Department of Health under the auspices of Medicare and Medicaid has the economic obligation to ensure that all recipients receive adequate attention at a reasonable cost. Unfortunately it would appear that the country's health industry is unable or unwilling to provide services at a reasonable cost. If the private sector continues to be unwilling to offer services at lower rates for Medicare and Medicaid patients, **the ultimate solution will be for HHS to construct new hospitals and medical facilities or acquire existing hospitals and facilities throughout the nation which will be staffed with HHS employees.** The national health system would be planned and designed to provide care for all Medicare and Medicaid patients.

It has been already proposed that all U.S. citizens should contribute to a National Health Insurance Program, the insured recipients would then have the choice of national health or the private sector for medical attention, but would be liable to the latter for all charges exceeding the established Department of Health rates.

The title *"The Health Industry – Penny Wise, Shilling Foolish"* is very pertinent to both the Health Industry and Federal Government programs. Our ancestors often wisely remind us that responsible ownership demands constant attention and maintenance resolving small problems in order to avoid major problems later. Such common sense applies to the individual and health. **Unfortunately society in the USA does not recognize the wisdom of our ancestors.** Small sums are not invested in guaranteed early health care attention for all thus eliminating the risk of major health problems and medical costs later in life. Society is obliged to pay the very high costs of delayed health attention which could have been avoided with the low cost of early health examination.

The scandal is that the problems of the Health Industry are so obvious and yet the citizen permits it to continue without protest or action. Everyone suffers from high costs, inadequate attention, and the unnecessary cost of treating individuals who did not have early health attention. Many western countries have national health and do not suffer the nonsense of this country controlled by selfish health industry entities and a corrupt political system. **Why is everyone mute?**

"There is nowt as strange as folk."

It is an old saying that possesses a very true observation. Richard pondered at the strangeness of his fellow people who imagine that they are intelligent and considerate of their fellow people. People who lack the intelligence and will to realize that their lack of action is harmful to their own quality of life.

What was the solution?

Richard shared his concern with a federal government health department employee, and demanded

"What is the solution?"

A disinterested man had no trouble answering that question.

"Well the health system is the product of the people. If they desire change it is up to them to demand Washington to make the change."

The insistent reporter responded.

"But it appears that Washington is subject to vested interests that represent only the powerful and rich medical and health industries."

The devoted loyal health department employee shook his head. This problem was not his concern. And regarding the inefficiency of government departments, he remained mute with tight lips.

Pork Barrels full of Pork

A barrel of salted pork was commonly found in 19th Century household larders, and was sometimes used as a measure of the family's economic status. An establishment possessing a high level of wealth and an over abundance of richness, could be described a place possessing numerous barrels full of pork.

The term *Pork Barrel Politics* normally refers to spending which is intended to benefit constituents in return for their political support of a politician, either in the form of campaign contributions or votes. Typically *"Pork"* involves funding for government programs with economic or service benefits that apply to a specific area and local residents but the costs are spread inequitably amongst all the nation's taxpayers.

Spending in such funding is classified as *"Pork"* when arranged as follows:

- Requested by only one chamber of Congress.
- Not specifically authorized.
- Not competitively awarded.
- Not requested by the President.
- Greatly exceeds the President's budget request or the previous year's funding.
- Not the subject of Congressional hearings.
- Serves only a local or special interest.

Pork Barrel spending is definitely a form of corruption with tax dollars used to encourage political favoritism and advance the careers of Washington insiders. This corruption is worsened through the lack of transparency and by the pressure from powerful lobbyists who represent vested interests.

Pork barrel projects were comparatively rare before the 1980s. Congress would fund general grant programs with the understanding that federal and state agencies select individual recipients through a competitive process or formula. The process was designed to prevent abuse and allocate resources on the basis of merit and need.

Then the procedure changed. Between 1980 and 2000 the growth of *"Pork"* accelerated enormously in the form of annual earmarks contained in Appropriations Bills. It is an abuse now so considerable that members of Congress rarely understand the projects and programs prior to voting.

The nature and character of the problem is not merely barrels of pork. Consider the Big Dig in Boston Massachusetts – the relocation underground of an existing 3.5 mile section of an interstate highway – the final cost **$14.6 Billion!** Just imagine in Alaska the **Gravina Island Bridge that would cost $398 Million** and would merely connect 50 residents of Revillagigedo Island and Ketchikan International Airport!

The Federal Government Office of Community Planning and Development (CPD) claims to seek to develop viable communities by promoting integrated approaches that provide decent housing, a suitable living environment, and expand economic opportunities for low and moderate income individuals. The primary means towards this end is the development of partnerships among all levels of government and the private sector, including for- profit and non- profit organizations.

The Department's work for Community Development covers a wide range of projects and programs and includes:

- **Washington politician Pork Barrel projects.**
- Community Development Block Grants.
- Appalachian Regional Commission.
- Senate Regional Commissions.
- Tennessee Valley Authority.
- Institute Museum Services and Library Sciences.
- Neighborhood Reinvestment Corporation.
- Rural Housing Service.
- Economic Development Administration.
- Office of NAVAJO and HOPI Relocation.
- Minority Business Development Agency.
- Small Business Administration.
- Low Income Home Energy Assistance Program.
- Advanced Technology Program.

Disability Relief and Insurance includes:

- Cooperative State Research, Education, and Extension Service.
- Raise flood insurance premiums on reputably flooded lands.

The purpose of Community Development is no doubt praiseworthy. Obviously communities with limited means could benefit through this Federal Government department arranging improved facilities, resolving local limitations in housing, job education for employment, general education and health, the provision of libraries, museums, recreational facilities, and general economic development.

However evidence demonstrates that many projects serve little or no purpose. **It reveals numerous Pork Barrel projects introduced by motivated Washington politicians which are more beneficial for non deserving interests rather than for the community.** Careful review of many programs, grants, and projects reveal that they serve no credible benefit to anyone other than the promoters and vested interests. One has only to examine the many sad American Indian Communities to conclude the failure of this Department and many of its programs and projects.

The small business administration defeats its own purpose of assisting small entrepreneurs by defining and qualifying applicants for assistance to include businesses of considerable enterprise and magnitude. The small entrepreneur is at a complete disadvantage and does not obtain the benefits that should be made available.

With regard to the Disaster Relief and Insurance Program, one should consider the predicament of New Orleans, ponder over the Katrina disaster, the painful slow recovery or part recovery of so many calamities, and question the value of this Program.

A very curious newspaper reporter approached a federal government employee, presented his concerns, and asked him whether or not his concerns had any validity, and if correct what was the solution. For example regarding Community Development all programs, grants, and projects should be phased out, and all future responsibilities transferred to the individual States where hopefully there are individuals far better qualified, equipped, and prepared to identify what is needed, to determine its ability to pay, and finally plan and manage such schemes. The local individual Taxpayer not only could determine and approve, but would be able to visit his local representative who no longer would be seated behind a mahogany desk 2000 miles away. Finally this arrangement would involve local financing which made both government and community cautious and responsible.

The loyal federal government employee was shocked.

"But what about me?"

In general the man in the street was little concerned. The problem was common place. It was Washington´s problem and they should resolve it.

"But how?"

The good man in the street avoided being trapped with this complicated question.

"Sorry man – I am busy."

The Police State

Over 12 years past, the New York Times published a thought provoking essay "When the Police Shoot, Who's Counting?" A few very significant paragraphs are presented as follows:

We like to think we live in the information age, when daily or even second-hand statistics on such fare as stock prices and the annual number of homicides are at our fingertips. For all the careful accounting, however, there are two figures Americans don't have; the precise number of people killed by the police, and the number of times police use excessive force.

Despite widespread public interest and a provision in the 1994 Crime Control Act requiring the Attorney General to collect the data and publish an annual report on them, *statistics on police shootings and use of non deadly force continue to be piecemeal products of spotty collection, and are dependent on the cooperation of local police departments.* ***No comprehensive accounting for all the nation's 17,000 police departments exists.***

The major reasons for the vacuum, the experts agree, are twofold. The lack of information on police shootings is attributable to the failure of police departments in many cities to keep and report accurate figures that distinguish between what the police see as "justifiable" shootings; those in which the suspect posed a serious threat; and incidents where an officer may have unlawfully fired at an unarmed civilian.

As for the lack of figures on the use of non deadly force, the situation is even murkier because there are no uniform definitions of force and no standard reporting requirements from one police department to another. One might rightly assume that the police do not desire to advertise their criminal acts.

Making matters worse, some police departments fail to report their shootings at all, and for some years, figures from entire states are missing. Although the 1994 crime act ordered the Justice Department to collect such data, there is no law requiring local police departments to provide i. Janet Reno, the former attorney general acknowledged this deplorable fact in a 1999 speech.

The lack of good data "is a national scandal" said Geoffrey Alpert, a professor of criminology and criminal justice at the University of South Carolina and a leading authority on police use of force "It's a scandal in the sense that these are public servants who work for us and are paid to protect us"

Bluntly Geoffrey Alpert is addressing a problem which is a national crime. 12 Years later little has changed. WHY?

Richard Homes knew the reason –despite claimed consideration of an obvious criminal problem by Washington politicians, all reports and conclusions were watered down, and recommendations have not been enforced. He would learn little more from the public – the crimes of the police were too well known.

He considered the pointless and criminal activity of police forces throughout the nation. Crimes had increased from 364 per 100,000 to 550 per 100,000 within the period of ten years 1970 to 1979. What could have possibly created such an enormous increase of criminal activity? It made no sense.

Investigation of the cause revealed that this increase of criminal activity had been due to the Federal Department of Justice deeming the possession and use of Marijuana to be a crime. Yet the possession and use of Marijuana is not considered a crime anywhere else in the civilized world. And this troublesome attitude applied to other social habits.

Just as troublesome was the attitude of the police, prison authorities, lawyers, and justice system who should be concerned with minimizing social problems rather than encouraging social strife through the fabrication and enforcement of unnecessary and illogical laws.

A number of very upset women attended the evening city council meeting with the purpose of protesting the unnecessary death of a young teenager. The young boy driving an automobile without a driving license had been apprehended by a city police officer. Seen later driving the automobile again, the police instigated a chase resulting in vehicles driven reckless and dangerous over city streets, and the final unnecessary crash and death of the young boy.

Richard Homes present at the hearing recorded the anguished and bitter thoughts of some of those attending the meeting.

"My son was such a good boy full of high spirits. Not a cent of badness in him. Now dead due to the completely unnecessary chase by the local cops. They murdered my boy through their callous thoughtlessness!"

"No young man deserves to die just because he has not got a driving license. The police are criminally irresponsible."

"Thousands die every year throughout the nation. The police ferment trouble through their unnecessary and aggressive response. The city would be better off having no police force!"

"This criminal nonsense goes on and on and on. Washington and the Federal Government must be made to enforce and control the police authorities everywhere. Both Washington politicians and government representatives have proved completely incompetent and unwilling to resolve this national problem."

"Every police officer should be made to walk his beat and know his fellow citizens. No officer should be allowed to drive a police vehicle except for emergencies. So many criminal incidents stem from sick mentally impaired people and highly excitable youngsters – the crime unnecessary and due to the reckless conduct of the police dealing with strangers."

There were many other unhappy and disturbing comments. Richard nodded sympathetically. So often he had heard similar thoughts in the past. Always the protests end up in the garbage can. **Resolution of the criminal conduct of the nation's police forces would never be resolved until the Federal Government acted positively in the interest of the people.**

Moving the American Way

The newspaper reporter was seated patiently in the waiting room. A magazine held in his hands had a critical editorial of the nation's transportation systems that demanded Richard's consideration. It commenced with a provocative question:

Did you know:

- *There are currently eight million (8,000,000) heavy and medium weight trucks operating on the nation's highways.*
- *Three million gallons (3,000,000 gallons) oil is consumed every day.*
- *Oil consumed daily is 15% of the nation's total oil consumption.*
- *29% Emissions of oil products is due to Transportation.*
- *A major cause of environmental deterioration, climate control, and climatic temperature increase, is due to the combustion and emissions of oil products. Already the nation is subjected to environmental disasters of considerable magnitude.*

Richard sniffed with annoyance. Although he was aware of the eight million plus heavy and medium weight trucks, the statistic of oil consumption was clearly wrong. Oil consumption for trucks alone must be about one billion gallons every day!

Errors in newspapers and magazines increase and increase through lack of responsible checking. He continued reading:

Question:

- *Is this method of transporting freight throughout the nation responsible and environmentally sound.*
- *Is it necessary to transport freight by truck if it is the major cause of environmental pollution.*
- *If not necessary, what methodology must be adopted.*

Efficient reliable environmental friendly and economic transportation is mandatory. *This commendable goal appears to be increasingly forgotten, and many modern transportation systems featured in other world countries are lacking in the U.S.*

Ground Transportation: _This nation has rigidly stuck to transportation by automobile and freight truck despite both vehicles being inefficient and extremely hostile to the environment. Highways, particularly interstate highways, are becoming incapable of supporting the mind boggling truck freight transportation and passenger automobiles that have been ever increasing in numbers. Years past perhaps one truck or truck trailer would be recorded for every ten automobiles._ **Now it is common to view one truck unit for every two or three automobiles, and all are travelling well over the sign posted speed limits!**

The highway transportation system is simply not designed for the current usage, and is a major cause of accidents, congestion, and environmental pollution. The highway infra structure is crumbling lacking adequate funding for maintenance. The majority of highway bridges require extensive repair or replacement.

It is quite apparent that special interests such as the oil and automobile/truck industries have persuaded Washington politicians to refrain from changing the current methodology of transportation and to ignore the environmental harm caused by this outmoded system.

Despite highway funding for interstate highways, congestion and inconvenience is ever increasing, and is clearly not the solution. Currently the federal government annual outlay for Ground Transportation is **_$62 billion_** _of which a miserable small part is allocated for high speed rail systems and mass transit._

Adequate funding for alternative transportation must be made, and a planned specific system announced. An obvious but no doubt unpopular solution is to transfer all road transportation funds to high speed rail systems and mass transit. Legislation is required mandating all interstate freight be hauled by rail. Also taxation penalties for industries that have centralized their operations throughout the country causing excessive and undesirable freight transport of materials and products.

The Department of Transportation's lack of intelligent planning and management is evident with its unwillingness to recognize the considerable environmental harm and heavy drain on the nation's energy resources caused by the current transportation systems.

Whilst other modern countries possess high speed rail systems for passenger and freight traffic, **_the U.S. suffers with a rail system that was appropriate for passenger and freight 150 years past._** _Amtrak sadly is obliged to use these aged rail systems, and is_ *incapable of offering speedy reliable travel whilst travelling on rail systems designed and shared with incompatible freight traffic. In order to resolve an obvious problem, considerable funding is required, and the transfer of road transportation funds to the rail sector should be mandatory.*

Mass Transit providing rapid clean and reliable transportation around and into cities is imperative. It is extremely unfortunate that so little funding is made available for a very important service that would make all major cities far more efficient, productive, and healthy.

An obvious solution is to impose increased taxation on vehicles and trucks, fuel, and vehicle highway usage. Interstate highway financing should be 100% paid by the user. As highly expensive vehicles used for passengers and freight are prevalent on the nation highways travelling at excessive speeds, it is reasonable that these users can afford to support and pay for the highways on which they travel.

In future a large part of federal government outlays for ground transportation should be invested in high speed rail and mass transit rather than on highways which should be financed completely by the user. The States should work with the Department of Transportation to ensure that the nation's passenger rail systems become an economic reality offering high speed rail systems connecting major city centers similar to that operating in Europe, Japan, and China.

The future financing of interstate highways should be provided by the private sector, whilst the financing of high speed rail and mass transit included in Federal Government outlays.

It should be noted that the taxpayer will eventually realize indirectly the economic and environmental benefits of high speed rail systems and sound mass transit systems. Also the transfer of interstate freight to the rail system, there will be a massive decline in unnecessary highway traffic and environmental pollution.

Richard placed the report by his side, turned, and asked a man seated nearby what was his opinion of transportation in the USA. Did he consider it efficient and environmentally friendly. The individual was working class.

"Never given it a thought. I have a car and never use public transport. I have to admit that traffic congestion is serious – all those heavy trucks are a major cause."

Later Richard boarded a local bus homeward bound, and asked the driver his thoughts.

"All this traffic is destroying the nation's climate with pollution. It is so obvious yet people persist in driving their cars although public transit is available. Possibly half of all my passengers are the poor. So you can imagine the small number of car owners actually conveyed by our bus system."

A truck driver at a local truck stop made a very significant and negative remark.

"Say man. Cut it out. Want to lose my job and living. Go and pick on the fat cats in their Cadillacs."

At city hall, the city manager demonstrated some concern. Most definitely the use of the automobile must be discouraged. And obviously the nation's freight long distance must be by rail. When asked for a solution to achieve those goals, his answer was not particularly satisfactory but final.

"Legislation by the Federal Government is mandatory to meet the desired changes!"

Richard resented the attitude of an overly paid public employee who thought the buck could be passed to others. Demonstrating the thought that such an important individual must possess ideas how this legislation could be achieved, Richard innocently asked.

"How will that be achieved?"

Alas the illustrious city employee shook his head irritably. As expected the city manager did not possess any ideas.

Money down the Drain

"What a joke. McDonalds has got ten million pounds of chicken wings in their freezers, and do not know what to do with them!"

Bill waved a newspaper towards his better half Shirley and laughed. Shirley, rather put off and facing a day of laundry washing, just stared.

"What´s funny about that Brains?"

"Well it is incredible. MDonalds is a very well run business. They just do not make mistakes. Apparently chicken wing meals were too expensive, and the public simply did not buy them."

Shirley absorbed that piece of information whilst she wondered how her leader, unemployed for years though no fault of his, still took a vivid interest in business information. She defended poor old McDonalds.

"Oh sure you can laugh but look at the terrible errors of government in judgment, lousy policies and programs. You cannot get work. Those errors cost this country a fortune and cause all this unemployment and dissatisfaction."

She left in a bit of a huff. The impending laundry wash was on her mind.

Bill sat back and wondered. Shirley was right. There had to be a solution. Over the past month he had made a list of government policies and programs that he considered should be adopted, **and would save the country an enormous sum of money every year.**

He pulled out the list from his desk drawer, and started to read below his positive heading:

Improving the Quality of Life and the Economy

It was a subject that must have been considered many times in the past. Surely Washington has discussed this subject. An interesting observation – one would imagine that our representatives have already examined, analysed, argued, and concluded every imaginary matter, and that appropriate policies and programs have been legislated.

However examining the sad state of affairs in the country one may conclude that appropriate policies and programs have not been legislated. In all fairness how can one expect Washington address these matters thoroughly when there are more important matters to deliberate. Important matters such as the needs of vested interests, their lobbyists, back room conspiracies, and the selfish demands of the few. Inevitably these demands absorb the attention of our Washington representatives with little time left for the legislation of policies and programs for the good of the people.

There were innumerable policies and programs that deserved consideration, included many changes which Bill thought represented considerable cost saving and should be adopted.

The Homeless

Proposal: Provide housing, health care, institutions for the mentally sick, education and job training, and assist 775,000 or more individuals become valued citizens contributing to the country's economic welfare. The current nation's outlay of **$46.5 billion to $77.5 billion** would be reduced to **$12.5 billion to $43.5 billion** and many thousand individuals would become valued citizens contributing meaningfully to the nation's economy.

Problem: It is deplorable that the nation claims to be a world leader 2009, and yet the U.S. Department of Housing acknowledges there are **643,063 Homeless and 1.56 million seeking shelter.**

About 1% of the adult population requires immediate assistance. It is a nation that is guilty of ignoring the plight of the homeless. A nation that refuses to acknowledge responsibilities for its own people:

- The deinstitutionalization of State Mental Health Services (Ronald Reagon).
- U.S. unemployment does not permit the unemployed recipient to seek job training education whilst receiving benefits.
- Foster home children are not given any job training, and may become homeless immediately they are released from foster care at the age of 18.
- A Federal Government that closes its eyes to problems rarely if ever discussed or resolved.

*The plight of the homeless is a subject we may possibly acknowledge or ignore, whether sympathetic and concerned or hostile and contemptuous. **Regardless shelving this problem is evidence that we lack economic intelligence, logic, and compassion.***

*The endless arguments hostile to the homeless and their problems shall be ignored. We will simply address the economic stupidity permitting this problem to continue. **Some unfortunate and costly features are as follows:***

- *The increase of garbage and crime on the streets, the spread of disease, the additional demand for street cleaning, garbage collection, and police surveillance.*
- *The strong possibility of the homeless being attacked and robbed.*
- *Drunkenness and despair.*
- *Prevalence of graffiti, property damage, and theft.*
- *The mentally sick and drug abuse sufferers incapable of resolving their ills.*
- *Hospital and medical care required for the sick and homeless exposed to the elements without adequate clothing and protection.*
- *Increased possibility of citizens being accosted and attacked by the homeless.*
- *The inconvenience and distraction of citizens due to homeless groups and demonstrations.*
- *Constant police interference and intervention at the direction of city authorities.*
- *The time and energy wasted by city authorities unable to resolve the problem.*
- *The incarceration of homeless through police intervention and the expense thereafter.*
- *The cost of public legal services representing the homeless.*
- *The public services necessary to supervise and administer the homeless placed on probation.*
- *The extreme difficulty for the homeless to obtain accommodation without conventional documentation. To obtain employment without a home address and stable records. The difficulty to open a bank account with limited funds.*
- *The economic loss to society of every homeless individual who should be a valued citizen contributing economically like all responsible tax payers.*

*Would it surprise you to learn that the annual cost of each homeless individual ranges from **$60,000.00 to $100,000.00**.*

*The total cost to the nation annually **$46.5 billion to $77.5 billion.***

And take note that the above costly statistics does not include the **1.56 million seeking shelter!**

One might question the number, the accuracy, and the validity of the **643,067 homeless** (2009) given by the U.S. Government Department of Housing but it is probably correct. Using a rough assumed check of 1000 individuals in every major city, 250 in the average town, and 10000 in small towns in each state, <u>an approximate </u>number would be **775,000.**

Solution:

Resolving the plight of the homeless would include:

- Provision of public housing (775,000 units) - **$600.00 month**   **$5.58 billion**

- Education and employment assistance (700,000) - **$10,000**   **$7.00 billion**

- Hospital and medical care (700,000) - **$10,000**   **$7.00 billion**

- Special institutions for sick mentally unstable (77,500)-**$100,000 $7.75 billion**

The total annual cost of addressing the homeless as listed would be about **$27.33 billion** – a considerable saving over the estimated current expenditure of **$46.5 billion to $77.5 billion.**

However no consideration has been given to providing temporary shelter for the estimated 1.56 million seeking temporary accommodation. A satisfactory solution would be the provision of temporary dormitory style accommodation at an estimated $12.00 cost per night per individual. The total outlay about **6.72 billion.**

It may be argued that the estimated sums are approximate. However the cost saving in resolving the problem is so enormous that rejection of the solution is not acceptable, and makes no sense. **There are so many other positive features.** Many thousands of individuals would become valued citizens contributing to the nation's economy rather than being a taxpayer liability. The streets would be freed of a national disgrace. The quality of life on city streets would be a pleasure. City services including hospitals, law enforcement, justice, and social care currently bogged down would now be able to undertake conventional responsibilities efficiently.

Real Estate Development

Proposal: *Ensure that the economic and environmental interests of the community are always considered and protected.* **Make it mandatory that the property owner is fully responsible for all Real Estate Development including planning, design, construction, and ownership.**

 Problem: *Real Estate Development throughout the nation lacks sound planning, suffers unnecessary ownership costs, and a short life. Often poorly managed and abandoned, a costly burden supported financially by the unfortunate local taxpayers. It applies to both public construction and private construction.*

Conventional wise business demands careful and responsible planning to ensure an economic and environmental solution that meets all concerns. Every eventuality is considered and biased defective decision making avoided. Once the implication of the chosen solution is agreed, business can then commence implementing the planned solution.

Throughout the implementation of the business plan, prudent companies set checks to ensure that the plan, conceptual ideas, and projected costs are rigidly kept. Finally once operational the business possesses valuable data as a reference, guide, and control whereby the project's purpose will meet the economic dictates of the initial plan.

This may seem common sense but real estate development rarely if ever adopts this wisdom. The end result a property that lacks adequate planning, a design often cheap and ill thought, significantly costly to own throughout its short life, and environmentally unsound. Major contractual and financial decisions are made with little or no evidence of accurate detailed construction and ownership costs. **Important design features that seriously influence the project's economy and environment are left to the biased and defective thinking of the architect and engineer during the design phase.** *Cost planning, design economics, economic design analysis, and cost control* **is notable by its absence.**

A common claim by the Construction Industry is that the designer has undertaken all necessary planning and cost control during the design phase **which is irresponsible and an absurd claim.**

- Architects do not possess skills in cost planning, design economics, and cost control; skills that demand the knowledge and practice of another very skilled profession.
- Architects, their business profit subject to time, inevitably make biased decisions, adopt inappropriate designs, and are often the cause of expensive design and contractual errors. In order to establish a sound design that complies to all known criteria, environmental, and economic concerns, such planning and investigation must be addressed at the conceptual phase. It is not feasible for the design office undertake such work because of limited time, business profit, and inevitable biased decision making.
- The property owner must possess a detailed conceptual design and accurate estimate before the design phase commences whereby he can make responsible financial and contractual decisions. Obviously this is not possible if the economic design planning, if any, takes place during the design phase. And of course the unwise property owner is simply gambling making contractual and financial decisions based on unproved and defective budget cost opinions.
- Without careful planning of the project at the conceptual phase and responsible cost control throughout the design and construction phases, the risk exists of the final cost being excessive, the quality of the design and construction inferior, and finally a project that will cause unnecessary environmental harm.

Imagine the disappointment of the unwise building owner to learn that the impressive plate glass and marble foyer will not be built, the hardwood paneled courtroom no longer economically possible, the carefully planned landscaped front area and pond now history. What had been a beautiful impressive structure is now a drab nonentity.

But far worse the community suffers. Throughout this unfortunate country there is a landscape of cheap shabby vacant developments – **a sad reflection of bad planning, lousy design, environmentally unsound, poor construction, and finally defective ownership.** No consideration has been given to the serious environmental and economic problems resulting from materials, components, and systems with a short life. Often it is heard that the problem is one of the owner – let him suffer economically. But that thinking is incorrect. The community, the nation, and taxpayers all suffer economically and environmentally as well.

Consider the ever caused economic problems through ill thought and defective cost prognosis. Economic problems that result in destroying carefully thought public budgets and the planned expectation of facilities and services. State, County, and City governments rarely understand or care the importance of accurate cost projects at the *conceptual planning phase whereby intelligent and meaningful economic decisions may be made before the design phase commences.*

Just comprehend the economic implications of these ruinous budgets:

Colorado Denver's RTD FasTrack Program Cost 2004 $4.7 Billion
2008 $7.9 Billion

*Marsella RTD general manager foolishly blamed the cause of the increased Program Cost of $3.2 Billion due to the rise in cost of construction materials! Allowing say 5% for annual inflation, the 2008 Program Cost would have been about **$5.7 Billion** not $7.9 Billion.*

Oregon Portland's Overhead Tramway Conceptual Cost Prognosis was about $16 million. The city was advised at that time that the prognosis was completely defective. The advice ignored. The final cost $57 million!

Colorado Windsor's Design Engineer's estimate for a steel storage water tank was $2.3 million. The bids $3.0 million and more. The cost increase absurdly claimed to be due to material costs.

Thousands of other examples of irresponsible cost prognosis take place annually throughout the nation due to property owners and developers, public and private, being incapable or unwilling to understand that construction cost planning and cost estimating is a highly skilled profession, and that designers architects and engineers have no expertise in such undertaking, and significantly due to natural bias, their design and cost opinions are inevitably defective.

Irresponsible property ownership destroys economically and physically the fabric of the community, and is unnecessary. Such failed properties, abandoned buildings, insanitary conditions, and vacant land, represent a serious loss of property taxes, and often a major environmental issue that may continue for many years. The inconvenience, harm, and cost to the individual taxpayer is considerable and must be prevented.

Urban sprawl can be viewed everywhere – property developments thoughtlessly located many miles distant from city and town centers. Everyone in real estate development is responsible – property owners, city planners, government bureaucrats, designers, engineers, contractors, bankers, accountants – the list is endless. The naïve city and town taxpayer subsidise these urban sprawl developments by providing city and town services and facilities that cost **$70,000.00 or more** for every residence in such developments. But what is much worse, the community and nation suffers from unnecessary traffic pollution and congestion. In Colorado it was determined that the average inhabitant due to urban sprawl **increased his annual mileage 4000 miles.**

Huge Box Stores are a recent feature claiming superior service and beneficial property taxes. What is not mentioned is that so commonly the city fathers have irresponsibly offered free or cheap land, low property taxes, and other incentives to attract these wretched box stores. And what is rarely acknowledged is that these box stores create unnecessary traffic and congestion, are often located on the town outskirts, and destroy the economic fabric of the existing downtown. Again, like urban sprawl, the local taxpayer can only blame himself for permitting his irresponsible town planners and bureaucrats recommend and subsidise an economic and environmental problem.

Solution: **The problems regarding real estate development can be resolved through legislation mandating that the property owner be held responsible for planning, design, construction, and ownership.** One has to recognize that standards of behavior and integrity in real estate development have deteriorated over the past thirty years – the cause ignorance, greed, dishonesty, and competition. The trend is a serious lack of responsibility and meaningful analysis addressing the real implications of a proposed development; the brushing aside of environmental and economic factors by individuals anxious to win design and construction contracts beneficial for themselves rather than the owner and society.

It will be necessary to mandate specific procedures and acceptable economic and environmental standards, and the owner thereafter held responsible for the project's procedures and standards. Although making the owner responsible for ensuring his project complies with procedures and standards may seem a burden, in fact the process ensures many benefits for the owner, the community, and minimizes environmental harm.

Legislation making the property owners responsible for the ownership of their developments with annual reports submitted to the local inspection authority will ensure sound property management and maintenance.

Consider Public and Private **annual** outlay for real estate development to be about **$1000 billion:**

- *Careful planning at the conceptual phase with skilled cost control throughout the design and construction phases will result in superior design and final construction cost savings of 2.5% to 10%.* **Savings of $25 billion to $100 billion,** *and for the individual taxpayer* **annual saving of $166.00 to $664.00.**

- *Careful planning with skilled cost control throughout the design and construction phases will result in minimal operation and maintenance costs throughout the ownership phase and achieve a cost saving of 1% to 1.5% annually.* **Savings of $10 billion to $15 billion,** *and for the individual taxpayer* **annual saving of $50.00 to $75.00.**

- *All real estate development by government (Federal, State, County, City) and Institutions using public money must always demand competitive bids prior to awarding construction projects. Awarding some favored contractor with his claimed unique skills must be stopped. This criminal practice very rarely has any justification* **and results in construction costs 5% to 10% above normal competitive costs.**

- *The award of design contracts by government (Federal, State, County, City) and Institutions using public money shall be based on the skills of the design practice, and most certainly not based on the design office submitting a low design bid. The design practice value is design creativity, skill, and time. A design bid well below reasonable remuneration simply invites low standards and a very poor investment.*

It should be understood that although immediate cost savings are described, just as important are the indirect cost savings realized over the life of the development, the long life of materials, components, and systems, the minimizing of heat transfer and low energy needs, acceptable low level of traffic generated, compatibility with the neighborhood, and minimizing environmental harm.

All the benefits described can only be achieved through responsible skilled planning at the conceptual phase whereby the owner can make sound contractual and financial decisions before the design phase commences.

Outsourcing of Manufacturing and Services

Proposal: Products and services have been outsourced by every conceivable sector to foreign countries over the past twenty years with the purpose of taking advantage of cheaper foreign labor. Currently 8 to 11 million are unemployed in the U.S and the rest survive on minimal wages. **The obvious and immediate solution is to impose high import taxes on all goods manufactured abroad and stiff tax penalties on the service sector.**

Problem: Although the moral of the nation's people is rarely considered, it is the very positive thinking of an optimistic population that unquestionably determines the country's economy and success. Thus the extreme importance of a population that is valued and enjoys satisfactory employment. In an intelligent well run and considerate society, all individuals should be valued and employed. **Currently 8 to 11 million are unemployed, morale is low, and the prison population two to three times greater than any other western nation.**

Millions of work occupations have been lost in recent years through Washington permitting major U.S. corporations outsource their manufacturing sectors and services to foreign countries. Over the past 20 to 30 years occupation work in every conceivable sector has been outsourced to countries such as India, Pakistan, China, Vietnam, Korea, Indonesia, Bangladesh, and others with the claim that foreign labor is cheaper.

This outsourcing of products and services reflects the nation's unfortunate values with decisions based on money however harmful it may be to others. This desire for cheapness has not only seriously injured the country economy and the unemployment of many million, it has destroyed the optimistic moral of the people, and has caused considerable environmental harm through increased international traffic.

With so many millions unemployed, **there is a corresponding lack of individual tax money revenues. If all 11 million unemployed were gainfully employed with an annual tax payment $1000.00 each, the nation's coffers would benefit by an additional $11 billion.** Revenues that could have been invested in well set out cities and towns, excellent mass transit, and the best education, health, arts, music facilities. Instead the nation is shabby physically and mentally; a nation gambling in stocks and shares, hedge funds, casinos, lotteries and other useless occupations; a nation that possesses shallow selfish beliefs, prejudice, and a lack of compassion for others.

The nation's loss of tax revenues is not the only liability caused by outsourcing. Consider the cost of the unemployed who no longer can afford medical and health care, the loss of their habitation, and other important social services normally taken for granted. That theoretical $11 billion loss in tax revenues is a minor matter when considering the state's cost of supporting the unemployed.

Solution: When the subject of economic growth and Free Trade is raised, we should be very concerned about the implications of such ideas. One should be alert aware of the current lack of work opportunity for many skills, the low wages so prevalent, and the reason it has been proposed. American corporations have realized that they can skirt their national obligations, business risks, and increase their profit margin by using foreign sources for their manufacture and service needs.

Economic growth defined by the number of Boeing aircraft or Ford automobiles or Apple I-pads may appear commendable but under no circumstance is it the answer. What is necessary is meaningful economic growth and employment in activities that employ every individual, not the select few, and such activities take place in the U.S. Growth and employment that will result in the improvement and the entertainment of the mind and quality of life.

There is no reason why this change in the nature and character of economic growth cannot take place. Outsourcing of products and services was the result of business and Washington politicians holding hands with little or no concern of the future unemployment of U.S citizens. **Washington has to change its thinking, a thinking not dominated by narrow selfish business interests.**

The immediate solution is the imposition of high import taxes on all goods manufactured by U.S. companies abroad. The tariff rate to be sufficiently high whereby it will deter U.S manufacturers from having their products made abroad, and they will return their activities to the U.S.

With regard to the service sector outsourced to foreign countries, all U.S. companies responsible for outsourcing must be charged a high taxation rate which will encourage them to transfer their activities back into the U.S.

True the profit margins of some U.S. companies may drop, and the cost of products and services may rise. But the benefit of full employment and a nation no longer suffering third world economic ailments will more than compensate the additional costs to the U.S. citizen.

Bill sighed and jotted down some numbers under the heading of **Money down the Drain.** According to his calculations government and private savings would be:

Homeless:	Savings	$12 billion to $44 billion.
Real Estate Development:	Savings	$35 billion to $65 billion.
Outsourcing:	Savings	$50 billion to $60 billion.

There were so many examples of public money waste. The disaster of illegal emigrants was considerable. The cost of simply supporting 3 to 4 million illegal families was probably costing the nation **$80 to $107 billion.**

Then there were the grim implications of a nation that does not apply intelligent wise economic growth. The enormous waste of materials and manufacturing input due to poor design and programs represents a terrible waste of money.

And it must be recognized that there is a serious lack of accountability of the Federal Government, State, County, and City Governments, and the nation's people. Irresponsible conduct and management that must represent 5% to 10% of the Nation's total annual outlay – **possibly $250 billion to $500 billion annually.**

Bill wondered if there was anyone possessing both intelligence and responsibility. He had just read a report listing the terrible damage caused by the National Security Agency, and the lack of credibility that the U.S. possessed in the eyes of world nations. Drone strikes, spying on foreign leaders and agencies, unwarranted aggression against foreign countries – the list of crimes are considerable. The NSA must be run by a group of imbeciles bent on destroying both the U.S and the world.

The world was facing major calamities which already had commenced due to CO_2 pollution. World carbon dioxide pollution levels in the atmosphere had reached a record high in 2012, well beyond the 350 ppm that some scientists and environmental groups consider as the absolute upper limit as a safe level. Ocean levels are expected to rise considerably, quite possibly many meters higher than present levels. With human development predominant on coastal edges, a major world catastrophe is eminent. Already weather patterns have changed radically, and conditions climatically have worsened in severity. **And yet people in the U.S. remain mute.**

Bill planned to show his calculations to a local newspaper reporter – he might be interested, and he might have an idea how this waste of public money can be stopped!

But before his fine ideas were promoted to the newspaper world, Shirley returned from the laundry.

"Well my loveable leader. Any hope getting a job?"

Poor dearest Bill bit his lips. How helpless is the ordinary man in the street when the country's economy is being destroyed by its leading businesses and politicians.

British always so British

Matthew Paris, a British monk of the 1200s, is famous for his diaries and records of England of his time. An interesting comment in a diary was that the French people considered the British to be strange uncivilized, uneducated, drunkards, argumentative, opinionated, and only too ready to fight and injure others rather than apply rational dialogue.

What is of considerable interest applicable to these unique individuals is that eight hundred years later *"Little has changed"*. If the good monk sauntered down the main streets of the historical city of York, in fact any main street of any town or city in Great Britain any Friday or Saturday, he would encounter raucous drunken scenes, curses and obscenities, screams and uncontrolled shouts and laughs, imbecile so called music blaring from within, illogical arguments and fights, and the revolting sick of those who have consumed too much.

No doubt he would shake his head both in despair and wonderment. Nothing has changed. Nothing has improved. Despite all the scientific research and discoveries emerging out of the Middle East between 800 and 1400, despite the remarkable findings of the few unique British, and the unrealistic platitudes and claims of the many unique British, very little has really changed.

Certainly, despite public claims of equality and equity, enormous numbers fled from Great Britain to North America for hopefully a better life. That hope was understandable and natural. What is very significant is that these very individuals, despite their perceived cause and experience of suffering, never changed their ways. Habits and beliefs, good and bad, never changed one iota.

True, like most of us, their explanation and blame centered on the property owners - the king and queen, the dukes and duchesses, the counts and countesses, the knights and so forth. A lack of representation, consideration, and compassion was a common complaint. Greed and self preservation dominated. One might simplify the status as being:

"What's mine is mine, and what's yours (if you have anything) is mine as well."

Well. That is enough about the neighbors of France. Hopefully the French people are enlightened by their observations of Great Britain over the past three hundred years the very aggressive British Empire, and its subsequent bankruptcy.

What is of considerable interest is the British now settled in North America. One would have thought that living in a country of plentiful wealth would modify and improve their thinking and behavior. Alas nothing has changed at all despite the abundance of natural wealth and the opportunity to observe the stupidity and greed of their cousins in Europe.

The British both in America and Europe claim to possess a series of values and institutions, personal liberty, free contract, jury trials, uncensored newspapers, regular elections, habeas corpus, open competition, secure property, and religious pluralism. And accordingly they consider themselves unique as advanced societies on this planet. And yet their behavior over the past three hundred years demonstrates the hypocrisy and stupidity of such thinking. It is one thing to pompously and aggressively claim to possess such values and institutions, but it is definitely another thing if one's conduct does not abide to such values and institutions.

It is true that many who represented Britain throughout the British Empire possessed the best of intentions, but it is also a fact that much of the empire comprised of countries seized by force, and a common purpose was commercial rather than providing the local people the questionable benefit of good British values and improved living standards. The history of the Empire is one of constant domination, war, and exploitation. Millions suffered. And the final outcome the virtual bankruptcy of Great Britain.

Empire builders with the best of intentions can demonstrate improvements in health and education of some colonies but inevitably one might conclude that such improvements would probably have taken place eventually if desired by the local people without the empire colonization. To be fair the British Empire builders lacked adequate education and understanding but that alone cannot excuse the commercial greed and harm caused by many. The so called spread of Western values was basically a series of military campaigns throughout the world, the basic intent being domination for commercial purposes, wealth, and power.

Perhaps the most striking feature of British thought and rule is that liberty has revolved around common law which was the product of the common people rather than the state. Freedom under the law and its benefits can be achieved by simply adopting the correct institutions and the common assumptions that apply with them. Democracy, as we should understand, is ideal in theory but can suffer very much subject to greed and corruption.

The reader is often advised of the declared wrongs of Autocracies with the common inference that we are fortunate to enjoy the advantages of a democratic institution. However one does not have to be a brain surgeon to realize the corruption and failings of democratic institutions. Unfortunately the failings of the democratic governments of Great Britain and the USA are rarely addressed or even realized by most of their citizens.

For example the foreign policy of both countries is very aggressive encouraged by the private commercial and industrial sector, with an unwillingness to solve problems through common dialogue, and a willingness to apply threat and actual aggression. Many million died throughout the historical creation of the British Empire. **Possibly 25 million have died directly or indirectly due to U.S. aggressive activities throughout the world over the past one hundred years.**

The end of the British Empire mid 1900s also coincided with the financial ruin of Great Britain.

What is so thought provoking is that the British in the USA had a front seat watching the demise and ruin of Great Britain and yet nothing was learnt. Thus sixty years later, the USA is bankrupt with a national debt of about **$19 Trillion - $19,000,000,000,000. Every Taxpayer, able or unable, is liable for a debt of about $126,000. Immediate settlement would be appreciated.**

Naturally an explanation is demanded. How could the world's greatest democracy fail?

Actually the explanation is quite simple. Study the Federal Government's Annual Financial Outlay approximately $4 Trillion for any recent year. At least 45% of all tax revenues has been granted through corrupt politicians in Washington directly or indirectly to corrupt vested interests and compliant federal government departments. If this corruption by Washington was prevented, and the people of the USA made wise decisions relating to national economic and foreign policies, there would be no national debt.

You protest. The USA has its responsibilities and its enemies. **$1 to $2 Trillion is needed every year for *"National Defense"*. The millions employed in the Services and those manufacturing *Defense Weapons* are all Patriots who have to be paid.**

REALLY!

The so called *"National Defense"* and the term *"Patriot"* are dishonest terms concocted by Washington politicians brainwashing the people to approve of the expenditure of enormous sums that benefit corrupt vested interests and politicians and finance universal aggression throughout the world.

WHY DOES IT HAPPEN?

Just look at a mirror. Yes you are to blame. And your cousins in Great Britain are just as guilty for the decline of their island. They permitted aggressive actions throughout the world, accepted the murderous recommendations of Churchill and others, and incredibly supported and sadly believed in their church which declared that *"God is on our side"*.

INCREDIBLE!

Not really. Mankind is basically corrupt and lazy. Whatever form of government exists, its success is subject to identifying and controlling prevalent corruption, and in turn it must demand and ensure that every individual citizen actively participates in every major decision relating to national economic matters and foreign policies.

When government fails in this very obvious need to eliminate corruption and meet the needs of the people, the people become petulant, pessimistic, and the country's economy weakens. The citizen must take on the responsibility of making decisions on all major economic matters and foreign policy, and stop leaving such responsibilities to corrupt politicians.

And the British in USA must start using their brains. Copying their cousins in Great Britain is most unwise. The notion that politicians are honest public servants is complete madness. Permitting Washington and the rich institutions to invest and corrupt the laws of this country can only end in this country's disaster. **America, in the eyes of these institutions, is for sale, and democracy with its current failings is the loser.**

Richard Homes shook his head with despair. What was the solution. The failings of the nation were many. Changes were necessary but how would they be achieved.

RICHARD´S FINDINGS SUMMARISED

Richard Homes entered Geoffrey Lancaster´s apartment complete with his recent findings. Rather uneasily he settled down in an armchair, set out an impressive pile of notes, and prepared to reveal and emphasize his observations.

"I have given you a summarized report of many interviews. My conclusion is that everyone in the nation is guilty of the current problems directly and indirectly through greed and selfishness. It reflects the nature and failing of the human race, a weakness which possibly will not change.

For that reason all current problems and their cause need to be identified, and a methodology devised whereby such problems can be eliminated equitably in the interest of the majority people rather than in the criminal interest of vested groups.

As you are aware, a considerable number of issues of major national concern have been raised. A common feature is the completely undemocratic process whereby Washington politicians, lobbyists, and vested interests have high jacked the annual taxpayers´ wealth of $4 Trillion, and distributed the money criminally to specific favored groups through dishonest decision making in the capital.

This dishonest undemocratic decision making is not in the benefit of the people. As the failings of the current decision making process is open to extreme interference of a few select groups, it is essential that all future decision making of the country´s wealth, policies, and programs are controlled and made by the people, and that Washington politicians no longer have any authority regarding the making of these all important decisions.

In my opinion there is no solution that can entertain permitting Washington to continue its current responsibilities – the scale of the dishonesty and criminal intent is too enormous to contemplate any acceptable reform."

Richard sighed with relief. The recent task and interviews complete, he was now a free man. Avoiding entrapment to another assignment, he shook his head when Geoffrey craftily wondered if he had any ideas how this change could be achieved and take place. Richard place both hands firmly on the table and stressed that he had completed his task.

"That´s your task Geoffrey. I have done my part."

Geoffrey smiled wryly. True Richard had indeed done his part, and his work was excellent. It was time now for the construction cost planner to invest some thought how the current problems could be resolved.

THE SOLUTION

Responsible Federal Policies and Programs are required.

Policies and Programs proposed for the benefit of the people of this nation are difficult to achieve whilst Washington politicians and government bureaucrats continue to make decisions that favor vested interests rather than the individual taxpayer. Furthermore all complex economic issues require **unbiased expert input and public understanding prior to approval.**

Past and current decision making by Washington politicians has been destructive to the nation´s economy, and simply encourages further graft and corruption with politicians working with favored business interests with little or no public input.

The tainted authority of the Washington politicians must be eliminated.

History suggests that the human race has never controlled its greed for material wealth and power, and only rarely has it controlled personal greed in consideration of others. It is obvious that federal policies and programs proposed in the interest of the masses are not possible whilst federal government decision making is made by Washington politicians favoring vested interests rather than the individual taxpayer.

The sad record of Washington illustrates what happens when the acts and omissions of politicians and bureaucrats are permitted year after year without adequate and responsible checks. Yes. You and I, individual taxpayers, are responsible for this lack of adequate and responsible checks. Without thought one might assume adequate controls and responsible checks could resolve the current problems. *Think again.* And it would simply involve consideration of a few numbers and a brief statement. *Think again.* **The current process of planning and decision making must radically change. No longer will Washington politicians be permitted to have the authority to make decisions.**

Sound planning, unbiased decision making, and responsible implementation is very much reliant on the initial process of determining the program, service, or concession. Unbiased individuals, some with considerable expertise, complete with public input are required to consider desired changes and ideas, and finally formulate an agreed proposition to be submitted to an appropriate and acceptable democratic process

Formalities similar to the following must be adopted:

- Federal Government Department representatives, private experts and public experts shall determine proposed programs and policies.

- Such proposed policies and programs shall be referred to Washington for further consideration with the understanding that the individual U.S taxpayer and citizen shall make the final decision of approval or disapproval.

- The Administration in Washington shall prepare a White Paper describing the program under consideration, its benefit, costs, and how it will work.

- **The individual U.S. taxpayer and citizen will study and vote on the initiative electronically recording majority approval or disapproval.**

This process will prevent Washington politicians from favoring special interests.

It is frightening to realize our inability to learn. We permit our government (Washington) repeat the same thoughtless aggressive and inconsistent foreign policies that have persisted over the past one hundred years. Just about every country, every government, every foreign entity has fallen prey to Washington's fabricated political and economic claims causing the unjustified death, injury, and economic demise of millions. It is a continuing conspiracy created by weapon manufacturing industries, agricultural industries, oil energy and generating industries, and other aggressive entities with economic objectives often supported by federal government departments. **The electorate basically is prevented from any involvement in this continuing conspiracy.**

Reason given for the conspiracies are many concealing their true purpose. Islam and many others entities not meeting present approval are the current scapegoats and declared enemy. Inevitably Washington will condemn others. Certainly the U.S has enemies throughout this planet – enemies self created through the hostility and aggressiveness of this country's foreign policy.

And of course due to this undemocratic and criminal decision making in this nation, we all suffer. The country's economy is in shreds. The environment ruined. There is mass unemployment and a lack of confidence. Our liberties and constitutional rights which have been the claimed hall mark of this country are threatened and some do not exist. Government spying and interference is prevalent. It is thought provoking that a dog rapidly learns through reprimands and guidance. And yet like sheep, we seem incapable of comprehension and action.

The time has arrived for change and action.

Our unwillingness to express an opinion and act is destroying our society. Like sheep our blank stiff and expressionless faces convey fear and resentment tied to thoughts not revealed through lack of courage. Politicians are permitted the freedom of making dishonest and destructive claims. Lies are transmitted with impunity by national papers, radio, and other communications. True most of us lie – for many it is a deliberate skill, for some possibly a work of art, reflecting the weakness of human nature. BUT regardless of this human weakness, it is no excuse for our lack of courage to both express an opinion and act. It is no excuse for our senseless fear to oppose those who are destroying this country and the world.

You are asked.

"Are you a man or a mouse?"

Geoffrey pulled out a clean sheet of paper, and carefully wrote a heading. It was brief, obvious, and demanded change.

"Washington – hands off Our Wallets and Our Lives!"

A major political change is required whereby the individual taxpayer and citizen (You and I) **shall make all future decisions relating to Federal Government policies and programs.** It will be particularly relevant to the function, operation, and management of all federal government departments and the economic implications therewith.

Political representatives in Washington (House and Senate) will continue to have their current authority but under no circumstance will these representatives have any authority in the decision making process. Such decision making shall be undertaken collectively by the individual taxpayers and citizens.

The objective is democratic. Change is required to eliminate the current unsatisfactory decision making of Washington tainted by lobbies and corrupt vested interests. The failings of the present system of decision making are costly, and not beneficial to either nation or its people. **In future decision making shall be made by the individual taxpayer and citizen.**

This change in decision making will assist in making major improved changes to current policies, programs, and subsidies, and such changes are estimated to represent a **cost saving annually of $1.5 to $2 Trillion.** Further cost savings **involving many hundreds of billions** can be anticipated addressing the homeless, real estate development, population control, outsourcing of products and services, wise economic growth, simplistic taxation regulations, and other important matters.

Indirectly many of the proposed changes will improve the quality of life – changes that would include increased federal tax revenues, equitable distribution of the nation's wealth, full and stable employment, meaningful and rational control of nation's prosperity and security, responsible accountability of all governments and citizens, the modernization of the nation's transportation systems, improved healthcare for all, better education facilities and scientific research, new libraries, theatres, and other desirable recreational facilities.

This proposed major change will have full hearted support of every wise individual. Communication by citizen organizations and similar organizations by phone, newspaper, magazine, email, face book, texting, television and whatever will make this essential political change succeed known and supported throughout the nation. Through legislation every taxpayer and citizen will have an economic stake whether in tax savings, improved public services, or both. By law every taxpayer and citizen will be obliged to take part in all future decision making.

No doubt the proposed changes rectifying the current defective democratic process will be vigorously attacked by the status quo, the embedded vested interests, lobbyists, and corrupt politicians. However the people must not allow themselves to be diverted by fabricated claims. **They must remain insistent that their interest and cause is purely the equitable and honest process of making decisions by the people.**

But are the proposed changes possible when one considers seriously the findings of Richard Homes? The nature of the man in the street is both selfish and apathetic. To seek and expect vigorous support for the proposed changes cannot be expected merely on words alone. That man must be convinced that he will personally benefit economically through tax savings, new and better services, and improved quality of life in order to participate in a positive manner.

Leadership must be politically strong, vigorous, and ever ending. The history of man is one of success subsequently overcome by dishonesty and greed. The legislative machinery established must recognize this failing and ensure its long term existence.

People have to recognize that an all important subject is avoided in the USA – how economic power functions in society. It is a subject discouraged by the nation's leaders and supporters; a subject that is frowned upon. The institutions responsible for this thinking are those controlling the nature and character of economic power; institutions that realize the danger of the man in the street possessing insight and understanding. Hostile institutions that are very much aware that such understanding would imperil their manipulation of the current political process, the loss of wealth and power, and endanger current social order.

The people of this country must and will in future determine the quality of life to be enjoyed by themselves and their families.

The man in the street yawned and sneered at Geoffrey Lancaster.

"That is all talk man. You will never get the people backing your crazy ideas!"

Geoffrey absorbed this hostile remark without reaction. It is so easy to criticize without offering reason or alternative solutions. However this and any negative comment required a positive response.

 Agreed the man in the street has a poor record in participating in the political process – there is also a sense, and a record to support it, that Washington has little interest, if any interest, in the common man. ***But that is precisely a sound reason that will encourage the common man to support a party (organization) that will eventually give him authority to determine his destiny.***

It may be claimed that the man in the street lacks the intelligence, education, and wisdom to make future political economic decisions. *Is that so! Just examine the credentials of the rascals in Washington. The man in the street is quite capable. Currently he has the unfortunate responsibility of voting for those dishonest representatives. His ability to vote for or against social and economic matters is more than adequate.*

The complexity of creating and controlling a new political party (organization) is too great for the man in the street. *Rubbish. The current political process controlled by two corrupt parties has only demonstrated their criminal skills in distributing the nation´s wealth to their fellow travelers, and making the possibility of a third party representing the people as difficult as possible.*

There is no evidence that the man in street has the energy and determination to radically change the political process determining social and economic matters. *What a ridiculous claim. True his lack of involvement suggests disinterest but is not evidence of his inability to be involved in the political process. Examine his ingenuity and skills in conventional business and other occupations. Clearly he is a satisfactory candidate. He simply requires the incentive to support the party´s declared aims.*

The only incentive that might encourage the support of the party by the man in the street would be economic benefit. *That is an excellent observation. Why should the man in the street express any interest supporting such claims – he has suffered hollow promises by Washington for many generations.*

It is submitted that the man in the street will support the proposed party for the following reasons.

- *The enormous waste of public money in federal government outlays - $1.5 Trillion to possibly $2 Trillion every year that support criminal vested interests and equally criminal foreign policies of aggression and interference throughout the world. That crime will stop.*
- *This enormous saving in federal government outlays can reduce the typical citizen payment of income taxes, and improve the quality of government facilities and services enjoyed by him.*
- *Education and Health facilities and services will improve, available for all, with services and costs similar to levels and standards elsewhere in the Western World.*

- *The subsidies received by favored industries – agriculture, oil, generating energy, transportation, science and space, justice, national defense, international affairs, and others shall stop.*
- *All industries shall be held responsible for environmental pollution, and such resolution and costs shall be addressed immediately.*
- *Pork Barrel projects and other favored projects design for the benefit of politicians and constituents shall be stopped.*

Now this reduction of Federal Government Department Outlays and the individual taxpayer savings realized through proposed changes are approximate subject to the nature and extent of the proposed changes. *What is far more valuable indirectly, particularly for the taxpayer's children, is the resolving of the serious environmental and economic harm caused to the nation and world through defective federal government policies and programs.*

The restoration of rivers, seas, land, and air is mandatory to overcome the terrible damage caused by agriculture, fishing, mining, energy generating industries, and other damaging operations and omissions. The recovery of natural crops destroyed through unnecessary agricultural practices, excessive application of fertilizers, and the intensive growth of crops. And the economic recovery of foreign farms ruined by ill thought U.S. subsidized crops and the equally ill thought so called Free Trade practices.

A very obvious question is placing a value to the cost of making good the extensive environmental harm already caused by Federal Government policies, programs and subsidies. The only cost opinion which is disturbing is the admission that the sums involved are enormous. ***And if changes do not take place the cost of making good the environmental harm will increase enormously, and that possibly such recovery will not even be possible. That may be the future faced by your children!***

There is no question that the man in the street will support the proposed party. The economic benefits and the improvement to the quality of life for his family and society are so considerable. His support will assist in the elimination of the criminal activity in Washington, and his involvement will dynamically determine the social and economic future of his family and nation.

Finally remember the sole purpose of the party is responsible determination and control of social and economic matters.